Krystonian Adventures

Translated by
MARK SCOTT,
PAT CHANDOK,
and
DAVE WOODARD

Publishers Note
This novel is a work of fiction. Names, characters, places and incidents are either the product of the author's imagination or are used fictitiously and any resemblance to persons living or dead, events or happenings is entirely coincidental.

Published by Mildonian Ltd., T/A Panton Int.

Illustrations by Bob Sparkes

Set in 12/13pt Baskerville
Typeset by Melton Kenner Associates Ltd., Stoke-on-Trent, England.
Printed by Rushton and Turner Ltd., Stoke-on-Trent, England.

To my son, Lloyd.
Remember what I've always told you . . .

"The extraction of dragon teeth can, I believe, produce some side effects. These include: complete loss of memory; regression to an infant-like state; severe neurosis; . . ."

'The Guardian of Health — Home Medicine for All.'

"When I think of the stresses and strains placed upon the performer, treading the dusty cavern floor alone . . . The roar of the granite-dust makeup! The smell of the crowd!"

Stoope Grumblypeg. Artistic Director, Cairn Tor.

"What you are about to witness involves no magic, twickewy, or illusion. It is merely a demonstwation of bwain-power which could be performed by anyone."

Pultzr. Genius in Residence, Cairn Tor.

"In that brief instant, when the great beast seemed transformed into a black, perfect silhouette framed by the burning sphere, I felt as though all time, all life existed only in its flight, and I envied the dragon its wings."

Kephren the Recorder.

"There is no other place that I would be on such a night as this."

Barloh the Pathfinder.

"Then roast her slowly over an open fire, basting occasionally. When almost cooked, add a few fresh roots, a pinch of wild spice, and brown on a low heat . . ."

An anonymous Snord (on the best way to cook a captive).

"I'm getting too old for this sort of thing."

Rueggan Amadeus Bartholong.

Author's Note

Those of you already familiar with Kephren's unfortunate
habit of vanishing from the tight corners his pen leads him
into, need no further warnings — you know what to expect!

For those of you about to start asking too many questions:
a day is still a day, snow is still snow, but I now know there is
something even more 'absolutely terrible' than any Hagga-
Beast.

KRYSTONIAN ADVENTURES

PREFACE

When first I began the task of recording all that is known of these lands and those who dwell upon them, I looked forward to a time when the last ancient manuscript had been translated, each and every race described, and all lore and legend thoroughly researched and documented. Then my days would be occupied in relating the doings and deeds of the present as they occurred. When the infirmities of age eventually made it impossible for me to continue, my successor's charge would then be one of simply maintaining a sequence of diaries and, when requested, providing the Obelisk Library with accurate copies of the most important or frequently used manuscripts. A night or two spent working by candlelight would then have allowed time to fully appreciate the beauty of the surrounding forest or, perhaps, to enjoy a leisurely evening in the company of friends.

How often since those days of optimism have I caught myself staring at my reflection in the wash basin musing, 'Ah, Kephren. So much for what you thought would come to pass!' For as the length and whiteness of my beard has increased, so have the number of reports, recently-discovered manuscripts and the frequency of parcels (now arriving almost daily via Dragon Transport), marked: URGENT. FOR YOUR IMMEDIATE ATTENTION PLEASE. Far from becoming easier, the demands made upon the official Recorder to the Council of Wizards have grown ever more difficult and time consuming.

Once, I believed my task might be compared in similar terms to a Trolle faced with the prospect of moving a mound of earth, sifting out stones as he went, from one place to another. No matter how large a task it appeared at the outset, sooner or later, shovel after shovel and bucket after bucket, the chore would slowly diminish and he could return home in the evening knowing that less awaited his arrival on the morrow. Likewise I saw, parchment after parchment and inkwell after inkwell, that my undertaking must surely decrease. How mistaken a comparison it has proven to be! Better that I had envisioned a hundred Trolles adding earth and a hundred more enthusiastically supplying more stones whilst a single one (me!) ran back and forth trying to carry it all away! And, whereas even the most stoical Trolle would have eventually thrown down his wooden shovel in defeat, I have not found myself able to lay aside my pen. I have sat, working at my desk until far into the night, when my heart has ached, urging me to throw on a cape, lock up my keldorr tree home and wander out into the forest of Keldorann for a few days.

Yet, beyond such moments of frustration and exhaustion and the occasions when self-doubt begs me relinquish my onerous task to one younger and more able than I, a deep, profound satisfaction still exists.

Whilst the Krystellate Obelisk stands and the Great Design continues, the names and events set down upon my parchment will be known long after I have departed to walk in other worlds. Aware, as I am, that written words can never completely reproduce an experience, I hope, nonetheless, that my chronicles will provide the imaginative reader with some picture of Krystonian life, its places, the events which have occurred there and, perhaps more importantly, those who dwell here. Above all, it is I, Kephren, who must ensure the many voices of Krystonia are never silenced, and the story of these lands continues through all time.

Extract from:
The Personal Diary of Kephren the Recorder

CONCERNING DRAGONS

No other race exhibits a greater diversity of size, shape, colour and temperament than do the dragons which inhabit the volcanic peaks at the confluence of the two great Krystonian mountain ranges of Kappah and Shugg. Here, where subterranean fires heat the rocky slopes throughout all seasons, dragons, so unlike in appearance they might appear to be completely unrelated, live side by side in their ancestral home — Cairn Tor.

Dragons small, dragons large, and dragons positively huge. Red, yellow, green and grey dragons. Smooth dragons and scaled dragons. Dragons with and without wings. Dragons who are invariably noisy and extroverted share caverns with dragons of a shy, retiring nature. Dragons known far and wide for their great wit and wisdom eat flank to flank with dragons renowned for their lack of either quality — but who, if truth be told, don't give half a mouldy charcoal biscuit what anyone thinks of them anyway.

You must understand; whereas two small, dark haired Trolles expect to produce small, dark haired children, dragon inheritance is a very different and more complex matter.

A pair of Grumblypeg dragons (i.e. lacking in both wings and scales) might never produce a single dragonlet which resembles either parent in the slightest. And, though it might cause concern — and some unseemly gossip — were the Trolle-wife to present her spouse with a tall, flaxen-haired daughter, dragon parents do not raise so much as an eyebrow when the same clutch of eggs results in Winged dragons, Mailed dragons (completely scaled) and Carbuncled dragons (partially covered with large, irregular scales) of different size, colour and personality. When you consider that the same parents who raised that most evil and maligned of all dragons, N'Grall, later hatched the docile and sleepy-headed Grazzi, it becomes impossible to ever take anything about dragons for granted again. (Although, there is evidence to suggest N'Borg's evil scheming coloured N'Grall's disposition whilst still in the egg).

Not surprisingly, this mixture of so many extremes in so close a proximity has given rise to enough reports and tales to keep me occupied completely (as others have been*) with their recounting. As many of my accounts testify, dragons are surely one of the most confusing, confounding, unpredictable and fascinating of all races. My chronicles would be the poorer without them.

*Translator's note:

It seems that Kephren drew both on this personal experience of dragons and the little known work of Bolo Kentha-Isthargon who was commissioned to write the definitive book on the dragons of Cairn Tor some generations earlier.

Kentha (to know) and Isthargon (the common form for any type of dragon) results in Bolo being referred to as a 'knower of dragons' or, what I might term in more contemporary parlance, as a Dragonologist.

Bolo's research was not well received by the Council of that time, and elsewhere he is named as Bolo Akenthra-Isthargon or Bolo-Dumfeoun (Bolo the 'unknower' or Bolo the 'dim-witted').

From what I have discovered, Bolo left the Obelisk after the Council refused to subsidize his researches any further. (He had, it is rumored, given away an entire storehouse of premium-grade charcoal in the space of a single season, in the form of bribes, to various dragons in return for their co-operation. The dragons got much the better of the exchange!)

He was also censured for stating before a packed Assembly that he knew 'less about dragons than he did the Council's Code of Practice'.

Only later, when others attempted to further his work, was it realized just how much he had actually achieved.

One chapter of his book, 'Dragons on my Doorstep', has been of particular interest, for it undoubtedly provided Kephren with both the information and motive to set at least one of the following accounts down on parchment. In this chapter, Bolo catalogues the likes and dislikes of dragons. He writes: 'The only thing to trouble any dragon more than extreme cold or having its internal boiler extinguished, is a toothache.'

GRUNCH'S TOOTHACHE

When the Grumblypeg dragon, Grunch, elected leader of Cairn Tor and President of Dragon Transport, refused to venture from his cavern and rebuffed all callers with a gruff, "I'm too busy. Come back tomorrow!", or, gruffer still, a curt, "Go away!", the other dragons went about their daily business unconcerned. Grunch, at his best, could be brusque. At worst, he was downright insulting!

Those unfamiliar with his complete disregard for social convention and etiquette have often been so affronted by his manners (or lack of them!) that they flatly refuse to speak to him again, and, whenever his name is introduced in conversation, turn an unusual shade of purple. But, to all who know him well — and I count myself as such — Grunch is beyond reproach. Though his ways may be enough to curdle a bucket of Mahoudha milk, he is, without doubt, one of the wisest, most trustworthy and industrious of dragons.

Thus, three days passed with everyone supposing Grunch to be hard at work on some new transportation contract, or busy reviewing the advance bookings for the advent of the Season of Harvest, which always required major rescheduling of the timetables.

They were wrong. Grunch had retreated to the darkest depths of his cavern where the smooth rock floor was hottest. Unbeknownst to his colleagues, he was nursing that most dreaded of dragon ailments — a toothache.

Now, whilst anyone who has ever suffered from a toothache would sympathise and make allowances for Grunch's temper burning on an even shorter fuse than normal, only some knowledge of dragon physiology — and, perhaps, psychology — can account for his unwillingness to leave his cavern and seek help. To this end, I must provide a brief summary on dragon teeth, followed by an account of events prior to Grunch's affliction being discovered ...

All dragons are born with teeth, the roots of which are of exceeding length. The portion above the gum is continually replaced from below as quickly as it is worn down, providing the dragon with grinding mills ideally suited for the crunching of the charcoal and grain mixture that forms their staple diet into a fine, digestible powder. Such hardwearing teeth, coupled with the almost obsessional dragon habit of tooth cleaning, means that decay is uncommon. The requirement for tooth extraction is even rarer — so anyone considering embarking upon a career as a dragon dentist would be well advised to think again. Only occasionally, in the throes of extreme old age (and dragons live a long, long time) might a tooth fall out on its own accord.

Grunch, being well acquainted with these facts, was, understandably, more than a little fearful that dislodging such a deeply rooted tooth would cause him considerable pain. However, compared to the constant discomfort of a raging toothache, the extraction would have been a small price to pay for the ensuing relief. There had to be some other reason behind his reluctance to make his predicament known.

And so it transpired.

Being the first of all Cairn Tor dragons who learned to read, and quickly realising the wide variety of knowledge it made accessible, Grunch had, over a period of many years, built up a sizeable private library — bolstered still further by books which had been provided on long-term loan from the Obelisk Library. When the nagging pain in the front of his upper jaw had broken his dreams, he had risen with-the birds, carried his stock of books to the cavern entrance and by the light of the early morning, had begun to look up every reference to teeth he could find.

After reading a deal of interesting but useless information concerning the dental configuration of various races, he happened to pick up an antique edition called 'The Guardian of Health —Home Medicine for All'. Surely, here was the answer.

Though the section dealing with toothaches had begun

hopefully enough by proclaiming in emboldened script: 'Toothaches — Quick and Effective Cures', the list of suggested remedies which followed —including the keeping of a colourful but highly pernicious little bird called the Wopknocker in the mouth for several days — were so horrendous and potentially fatal for the poor sufferer that even the toothache seemed mild in comparison. Grunch felt sure the author had not based his cures on first-hand experience.

Worse followed. Unknown to Grunch, the author of 'The Guardian' had belonged to a small group of despicable and thoroughly misguided individuals who, as they put it, 'practiced the Noble, Ancient and High Art of Dragon-Calming'. Thankfully, this pastime has long been highly illegal, for it involved reducing noble beasts to quivering, terrified slaves. The victims were invariably young (and thus, less dangerous) dragons; and many more died, as a result of the tortures they were subjected to, than were ever 'calmed'. Had Grunch been aware, he would, you may be certain, have reduced the book to ashes on the spot. But, having failed to notice anything to arouse his suspicions, so desperate was he to find a practical cure, Grunch read on until his eyes lighted upon the fateful last paragraph which had been included as a footnote at the very end of the toothache section. It read:

The extraction of dragon teeth can, I believe, produce some side effects. These include: complete loss of memory; regression to an infant-like state; severe neurosis . . .'

I am certain any of these side-effects were a direct result of the terrible methods employed in the extraction rather than the physical loss of a single tooth. But poor Grunch was in no state to make any such supposition. He saw only the words which carried the threat of the awful consequences likely to attend the removal of the tooth.

He slammed the book shut. He would just have to suffer in silence and hope, somehow, that the toothache would go away.

Of course, toothaches never 'just go away', and Grunch spent three sleepless days and nights with his snout pressed to the hot floor of the cave before help arrived.

You may have read elsewhere in my chronicles about the wizard, Graffyn, and how he once bettered Grunch in a business deal — the first and last time anyone had managed such a feat. Since then, any negotiations between the two have always been a potentially explosive affair. However, business aside, the mutual respect the dragon and wizard hold for each other has developed into what can only be described as a 'competitive friendship'.

So when, on the fourth morning, Graffyn had arrived at Grunch's cavern to finalize the transport arrangements for a party of Apprentices, he ignored all of the dragon's attempts to turn him away and marched straight in.

"I have not travelled all the way here to be told to come back tomorrow!" he declared upon entering. "Like yours, my time is extremely valuable and I'm more than a little annoyed that . . ." Graffyn's words trailed off. In the gloom of the caverns interior he could just make out Grunch lying on his side. "By my beard! What ails you, Grunch?"

"Nothing . . . a headache . . . go away," the dragon mumbled between clenched teeth.

Graffyn approached and bent down close to Grunch's head.

"Go away. Leave me alone," said Grunch, miserably.

"I shall do no such thing," retorted Graffyn. "At least not until I've found out what's really wrong with you. Now come out into the light so I can see you better."

(Not only was it too dark for Graffyn to see properly, the cavern floor was so hot he feared the soles of his sandals might be melting!)

"Please, let me be. I just need some peace and quiet." This was followed by a barely stifled groan which left Graffyn in no doubt that something was very wrong.

"If you don't move to where I can see you, I'm going to ask Spyke to come and sing you a lullaby," he said.

"That's a cheap trick," moaned Grunch. "It's bad enough trying to sleep when you've got a toothache, without you threatening to inflict earache into the bargain."

"Ah, ha! So, it's a toothache!" exclaimed Graffyn, triumphantly.

Grunch made no reply save another groan.

"Come. Just let me take a look at it," offered Graffyn, his voice now low and reassuring. "I might be able to help."

It was useless to resist further. Slowly, Grunch eased himself up onto his feet and shuffled to the entrance of his cave, grunting with pain each time he took a step.

"You look awful!" Graffyn exclaimed, involuntarily, upon seeing the dragon's bloodshot eyes and swollen face.

"If all you're going to do is throw out insults I'll go back and lie down," snapped Grunch.

"Stop grouching and open wide," ordered Graffyn, quickly adding, "And don't forget to swallow your flames!"

No sooner had Grunch complied than Graffyn popped his head straight inside the dragon's mouth. From a distance, it must have looked as though the wizard was in the process of being swallowed whole! Grunch felt Graffyn fumbling on his wizard's pouch as he took out a krystal and muttered a few spell-words which caused it to glow with a soft light. Subsequently, that too vanished inside Grunch's gaping mouth.

When Graffyn eventually reappeared he was shaking his head.

"Dear me. You've got a real stinker there," he pronounced. "Looks as if a piece of charcoal has embedded in the gum and caused an abscess beneath the tooth."

"So much for the diagnosis, what about the cure?" asked Grunch, moodily.

"Well, it's not exactly my subject," replied Graffyn, "but I'd say it'll have to come out."

"No!" exclaimed Grunch, visions of being reduced to the mental capacity of a dragonlet flashing through his mind. "No! The tooth must stay!"

"If the tooth stays, then so does the toothache," replied Graffyn. "You can't go on like this. How can you hope to run a successful business in such a condition?"

Grunch knew that Graffyn was right. In his present condition Dragon Transport would fall into disarray within days. He must either transfer leadership to another or take the risk of having his tooth pulled. It seemed, to quote a dragon saying, that Grunch was caught with his tail in the thorns.

"Yes. It'll have to come out," he conceded glumly.

"Of course, I could be wrong. I want a second opinion. In the meantime, press this krystal against your cheek; it should ease the pain a little until I return," said Graffyn.

Grunch did as instructed. Incredibly, no sooner had the krystal touched the affected area, that the pain subsided to a dull ache. The dragon almost — almost — smiled with relief.

"Now," said Graffyn, "which of your dragons can be placed at my disposal?"

"They're all booked," retorted Grunch, flatly. "You'll have to walk."

Graffyn stared in disbelief. Here he was, going out of his way to try and help Grunch, and the dragon was still being difficult.

"What about that one?" said Graffyn, motioning towards a dragon who was stretched out on a rock enjoying the sunshine. "He doesn't seem to be desperately overworked."

"That's Hulbert. It's his day off."

"You mean it was," Graffyn retorted before striding over to the unsuspecting dragon.

Grunch watched as Graffyn explained the situation to Hulbert, the wizard pointing frequently over to where he was sitting, tail holding the relief-giving krystal to his cheek.

Presently, Hulbert rose to his feet and stood patiently while Graffyn scrambled onto his back.

"Don't worry, I'll be back soon!" shouted Graffyn, cheerfully.

"That's done it," muttered Grunch, as several dragons, attracted by Graffyn's shout, noticed their President sitting at the entrance of his cavern, krystal to cheek, and looking decidedly the worse for wear. "Now I won't get a moment's peace."

Grunch was right. Hardly had he settled down to catch up on some of his lost sleep than the first callers began to arrive. Within no time, news of his toothache reached the ears of every dragon in Cairn Tor — most of whom took it upon themselves to join the swelling congregation encamped beyond the entrance of his cavern. As the assembly grew in size, so did the din, as every dragon strove to make its voice heard above the rest. Soon, the inside of Grunch's cavern, along with the inside of his head, resounded and redoubled with the noise.

At length, when it became clear that they were not going to run out of curiosity before he ran out of patience, Grunch got to his feet and sallied forth.

"Quiet!" he boomed — an action which necessitated the removal of the krystal and sent a jarring pain into his head.

There followed a protracted bout of "Shh — Sshhing" sounding very much like a large geyser blowing off an excessive head of steam, before the assembled dragons fell silent. All eyes now regarded Grunch expectantly.

"I fail to see the reason for such excitement", he began. "I have a minor tooth complaint that will soon be remedied and, grateful though I am for your concern, I would prefer you to let me sleep awhile. There is no need for all this unnecessary fussing."

"Dear Grunch, I have come to offer only my help and comfort," said the matronly Flayla, various small dragonlets clustered about her. "Great Aunt Florimell swore the best thing for a toothache was hot lava soup three times . . ."

Flayla's words were swallowed up faster than her Great Aunt's soup in the ensuing welter of shouted advice and proposed cures. Every dragon, most of whom had not the slightest notion of what a toothache was, had an opinion they just had to share.

This time, Grunch kept the krystal firmly in place and affected a silence by fixing each dragon in turn with a withering stare.

"You may rest assured," he growled, "that I expect expert help to arrive at any moment."

"I'm not sure I'd call Gyum the Hermit and his trained Wopknocker expert help," snorted Flayla, derisively.

"What!" bellowed Grunch, the mere mention of Wopknocker birds enough to cause an involuntary stiffening of his tail. "Who told you that?"

"Hulbert," Flayla replied, flatly. "I spoke to him and Graffyn on their way out."

Grunch was visibly shaken. How could he have been so stupid as to entrust his welfare to that trickster, Graffyn!

"Don't just stand there," he snapped, "fetch the hot lava soup!"

Though Grunch gulped down enough of Flayla's lava soup to empty a small volcano, it had no effect beyond giving him a sore throat, a rumbling stomach, and generally making him yet more miserable.

It did not end there. Having given Flayla her chance to cure him, the other dragons clamoured to be allowed a similar privilege. And what a variety of imaginative cures they devised! Most were unorthodox. Some impractical. A few were simply crazy!

Nowhere was more inventiveness shown than in the solutions proposed by a small group of young dragons who sat some distance from the others for fear the adults might try and steal their ideas.

Spyke, the adolescent dragon renowned more for his singing (!) than any mental prowess, hit upon the idea of tying one end of a woven grass rope to the tooth and then, after tying the other end about his tail, taking off at high speed.

Pultzr, a young Carbuncled dragon of prodigious intellect who spent most of his time with his snout in a book, advised against such an attempt.

"A bwight idea," he conceded, "but I'm afwaid it is impwactical. I estimate the force wequired to dislodge the tooth to be gweater, by a coefficient of two, than the maximum thwust

Spyke's wings could pwoduce."

For a time they toyed with the idea of replacing Spyke with a heavy boulder and pushing it down the steepest slope they could find. Again, it was Pultzr who cautioned against the idea on the grounds that if the tooth did not instantly pull free, Grunch, boulder and all would roll down the slope together. When Pultzr further asked them to consider the severity of Grunch's reaction to such a failure, the plan was quickly dropped.

Stoope, an adult Grumblypeg who, it must be said, much prefers the company of youngsters than dragons of his own age, had, all the while, concealed himself behind a large boulder in order to eavesdrop on the young dragons. Unable to contain himself any longer, he suddenly reared up from his hiding place, frightening the youngsters half out of their wits.

"I know!" he shouted, gleefully, "Why don't we cut his head off? Then he'll never get a toothache again!"

"Wow! Way out, Stoopey!" exclaimed Spyke.

As the rest of the dragons fell about in fits of giggles, Pultzr looked slowly from Stoope to Spyke and back again, shaking his head. Sometimes you just had to wonder.

When the group finally regained their composure, Shadra, who had hung upon Pultzr's every word, reached out and touched him lightly on the paw.

"What's your idea, Pultzr?" she cooed. "You're bound to have the best one."

Pultzr suddenly felt as if his internal boiler had raised its temperature by several degrees, and he stared at the ground as if it held some new fascination for him.

"I ... er ... I ... have sevewal possible hypotheses," he stammered, "that wequire further wesearch before I pwesent my conclusions ... er ..."

"Oh, Pultzr! You're so ... so clever!" exclaimed Shadra, adoringly.

This was too much for Pultzr to endure, especially when he noticed Stoope and Spyke wearing idiotic grins and trying their utmost not to laugh openly.

"So . . . I'd better get back to my books," he said, all in a rush. "They are sure to pwovide the solution to the pwoblem." He began to hurry away to his private cavern before Shadra could detail him further, leaving her to look longingly after his rapidly diminishing form.

"What a dish!" she sighed, wistfully.

Now it was Spyke and Stoope's turn to shake their heads in wonder.

Under the watchful eye of Flayla, the female dragons had subjected Grunch to a plethora of infallible cures — all of which were remarkable only for their complete lack of success. Yet the females had revelled in the whole affair. Grunch had never been so vulnerable, and each dragon maid in turn had forced their particular powder, potion or elixir upon him as though he were nothing more than an oversized, slightly stubborn dragonlet. It was, they all agreed (except Grunch, of course) the social event of the season.

In short order, they took over his cavern completely. Those not engaged directly in the administration of the next cure had made themselves very much at home. Some sat in groups, knitting and making small talk. Others took it upon themselves to begin cleaning the cavern. Much to Grunch's annoyance, they swept the floor and sorted Grunch's books into neat piles that left his reference system in ruins and, to cap it all, hung posies of dried flowers from the walls.

"What a difference the touch of a female paw can make to a place," said Flayla, looking about approvingly.

This state of affairs might have continued indefinitely had not one of the cures brought the party to an abrupt end.

One of the females, in the process of applying crushed herbs to her patient's gum, touched against the affected spot causing Grunch to wince with pain and inhale sharply. Virtually the entire contents of the bowl she held disappeared up his nostrils. A sneezing fit to end all sneezing fits ensued, tongues of flames and clouds of smoke accompanying each sneeze.

Within moments, every female had fled from the cavern; all except Flayla who was doing her utmost to comfort a tiny dragonlet which had been awakened by the rumpus and was bawling loudly. Worse still, every time Grunch sneezed he dropped the krystal and added his own groans to the infant's cries.

"Out! Out! OUT!" Grunch ordered, upon seeing Flayla amidst the slowly dissipating smoke billows.

"Don't you dare shout at me!" she scolded. "Look, you've upset little Culpy, you nasty, horrid dragon." As if on cue, Culpy let out another ear-splitting wail.

"There, there," soothed Flayla. "Don't fret so; Flayla won't let the mean, nasty dragon shout at poor little Culpy."

"Alright! Alright! I'm sorry! Now please, please just leave me alone."

Grunch gave Culpy a hurried tickle beneath the chin in the hope that it would restore the silence. Miraculously, it worked, and the wailing subsided until only the occasional sob issued from the dragonlet.

"Now, that's better," breathed Flayla, softly. "Culpy and Grunchie are friends."

Before he had any opportunity to object, Flayla thrust Culpy into Grunch's paws.

"What am I supposed to do with this ... err ... him?" protested Grunch.

"Sshh!" cautioned Flayla. "You'll set him off again." She smiled and added, "Look at you. You're a natural!"

Grunch said nothing. He sat and glowered moodily.

Taking up Culpy's blanket, Flayla wrapped it tightly around Grunch's face, tucking the krystal beneath the folds.

"See, she said, standing back to admire her handiwork. "Now you can sneeze away and your precious krystal will stay put."

"What I must look like!" complained Grunch — though he was secretly rather impressed by Flayla's resourcefulness.

"You look like what you are," she returned. "A big baby. Now sit and wait quietly for Graffyn to arrive and don't cause any more trouble.

Grunch sneezed, a small spear of flame flashing from his snout and setting light to one of the dried flower posies.

Flayla shot him an accusatory look, as if to say, 'You did that on purpose!'

"Sorry," he gulped, looking extremely guilty.

Gently, Flayla lifted the sleeping dragonlet from Grunch's paws and walked out of the cavern, leaving him to contemplate the imminent arrival of the Wopknocker. One thing was for sure — male dragons never grow up.

For a while, Grunch was left in peace. He tried several times to sleep, but he no sooner closed his eyes than the image of a gigantic Wopknocker sprang up between him and the warm, safe realms of dream-land, or a violent sneezing fit shook his entire frame. Eventually he gave up and decided to occupy himself about the cavern.

First, he removed the scorched remains of the flower posies from the walls — some of which still smoked and smouldered. Next, he unfolded several large timetables, laying them out upon the floor in order to create the impression of activity. Finally, he began the task of returning his books to their former state of organized disorder — all, that is, except for one.

When he came across 'The Guardian of Health' he had been unable to resist a most uncharacteristic impulse and had thrown the offending tome forcefully out of the cavern, watching with satisfaction as it bounced along the broad ledge outside and vanished over the edge of a precipice.

It was not long before he managed to erase almost every trace of female interference and returned his cavern to the unmistakable clutter which often seems to accompany confirmed bachelordom. The only thing he retained, and that was a matter of temporary convenience, was Culpy's blanket about his face.

He was carefully replacing the last few books and wondering

what to do next when a purposeful cough made him turn. Standing just inside the entrance was Pultzr.

"Gweetings, Gwunch," he said, good naturedly, as soon as he saw he had attracted the adult dragon's attention.

"Hmm?" Grunch sat back, resting on his tail, and waited for Pultzr to continue.

"I have ... umm ... I think I might possibly pwovide a solution to your pwoblem," he offered.

In his present mood, had any other dragon approached Grunch he would have dismissed them in short order. But Pultzr was different. He might look like just any other young Carbuncled dragon in size and shape, but the resemblance ended there. He was, without question, phenomenally intelligent, and Grunch knew he was not given to calling on anyone unless he considered he had something important to say.

"Well? Don't stand there dithering," said Grunch, being deliberately grouchy. "I've got work to do."

"I believe I can wid you of your toothache both quickly and with a minimum of pain," he started.

"Thanks — but no thanks," declined Grunch. "I've had my bellyful of so-called cures today."

"Yes, I've heard. But don't you see, evwyone has made a fundamental mistake. They have attempted to cure the pwoblem, not wemove it completely."

"So?"

"My method is diwect and quick."

"So? Dear me, Pultzr, I do wish you'd stop walking around the boulders and get on with the explanation."

"Alwight. Basically, I intend to blow the tooth stwaight out. Evewything is pwepared. All I now need is you, and the loan of your kwystal."

Grunch raised an eyebrow. "How do I know my head won't be removed along with the tooth?"

"I can pwomise you, all my calculations have been checked and double-checked. Please, Gwunch, all I'm asking is to show you how it works on my demonstwation model. If you then decide to take your chances with the Wopknocker, I will understand."

"A demonstration model, you say?" The little dragon must have worked on his project all day.

"Yes. A scale model to wepwesent your upper mandible."

"Mandi . . ."

"Your jaw."

"Yes, of course . . . So, Pultzr, you're confident of success?"

"I am." Pultzr's emphasis on the reply left his belief in no doubt.

"Well, the least I can do is take a look. There's no harm in that I suppose," Grunch finally agreed.

Pultzr's visit had not gone unnoticed. As soon as she had made sure he was not thrown out as quickly as he went in, Shadra ran around informing every dragon she could find that Pultzr was about to cure Grunch's toothache once and for all. This latest twist in the saga, fuelled by Spyke's prediction that Pultzr was sure to attempt something spectacular, appealed to the curiosity of the inhabitants of Cairn Tor.

Grunch had scarcely squeezed his bulk into Pultzr's cramped quarters before a large, noisy crowd had gathered once more. Expectations were running high.

(The fate of this single tooth had become an attraction unrivalled by any since Stoope had attempted — after much advance publicity and hype — to swallow his own tail. That show had cost two charcoal biscuits per head and had resulted in many dragons demanding a refund when it was discovered that Stoope had fashioned a fake tail from edible lava. Personally, I think he deserved at least three charcoal biscuits per head for his inventiveness and ingenuity.)

"You might emerge from this as a hero," said Grunch, when the sound of the crowd reached his ears.

"Hewoes may last but a day; discovewy may endure for an age," replied Pultzr, humbly.

'My word,' thought Grunch, 'He's even quoting Azael's

zr proposes a scientific solution to Grunch's toothache . . . with expensive results!

Creed, now.'

"Now, look . . ." Pultzr cupped a small amount of dark powder in a paw and held it up so that Grunch might see. "I take this, pack it into this hollow pebble, like so . . ." He carefully trickled the powder into a hole drilled in one end of a small, black pebble. "Then I seal it with a few dwops of keldorr wesin."

Grunch watched with interest, marvelling at the self-assurance with which Pultzr went about his task.

"Next I stwap it to the tooth on this model."

"That looks nothing like my snout!" Grunch interrupted, pointing to the length of rudely fashioned wood from which a single triangular peg protruded.

"It will suffice," answered Pultzr, brushing Grunch's query aside. "Now, I am weady for the kwystal, if you please." Pultzr held out his paw.

"Alright," said Grunch, retrieving the shining stone from between the folds of the blanket about his head. "But make it quick, will you? My toothache is agony without it."

"It will be over in a flash," Pultzr assured. "Just cover your eyes and . . .

A thunderclap loud enough to rival any caused by one of Rueggan's experimental malfunctions erupted from the cave and shocked the crowd to the ends of their tails, momentarily tranfixing them as though they were sculpted from stone. It was followed, almost instantly, by a shower of vermilion sparks which fell down upon the assembled dragons in a jewelled rain and sent them diving for safety. A plume of yellow smoke crept lazily from the cave entrance and formed itself into a thick cloud, hanging motionless in the air. Then silence.

"Wow!" shouted Stoope, his head still buried protectively in his paws, "I could use that in a show!"

Somewhere, quite possibly from beneath Flayla's generous midriff, there came the muffled but unmistakable sound of Culpy, crying.

Cautiously, the dragons picked themselves up, dusted the ash from their hides, and peered towards Pultzr's cave.

"Let's go see!" urged Spyke.

"After you," Stoope replied, never one to chance his hide unless it was for the benefit of an audience.

Finally, a group of male dragons decided they had a duty to investigate in case their President and Cairn Tor's resident genius had both gone up in smoke. They had barely taken two steps when a loud sneeze was heard. Grunch's head appeared, Culpy's blanket flapping loosely about his neck. He emerged, quickly followed by Pultzr —both wreathed in smoke. They looked dishevelled but unharmed.

"What are you all gaping at?" he thundered. "I've told you all, GO AWAY!"

"We were just coming to see if you needed help," said Stoope.

"Why should I need your help?"

"The explosion . . . your tooth . . .?"

"This little thing?" asked Grunch, extending a paw. There, roots and all, lay a single large tooth.

"My word, he's done it! Pultzr's done it!" Flayla exclaimed. Pultzr looked embarrassed.

"You see," said Grunch, "As I have told you all so many times, there is nothing to beat a book. Don't you agree, Pultzr?"

"Err . . . yes. Quite so." replied Pultzr, looking rather sheepish.

Pultzr was soon pressured into giving a full account of the events leading to Grunch's cure. Whilst Grunch would have been quite happy to leave everyone guessing, Pultzr could not bear to hear himself praised for something not entirely of his own doing.

He had underestimated the power of the krystal and the unstable nature of his newly discovered compound. Instead of the small, controlled explosion he had anticipated, the initial energy release had been so great it instantly ignited the reserve stock he had put to one side for further investigation. This had resulted in the single large explosion they had all heard. Fortunately, the main blast escaped through the cave entrance and the two dragons had merely been thrown against the wall as it rushed by them.

"And when Grunch hit the wall his tooth fell out," Spyke suggested.

"No. Not exactly," Pultzr corrected. "It was, in fact, a book which I had been weading earlier that hit Gwunch on the snout and knocked his tooth out."

"Well, *it was your book* that did the trick, Pultzr," Shadra gushed, determined he should retain some credit for his part in the proceedings.

"Again, not exactly. By a stwange coincidence I found it earlier today when I was on my way to Gwunch's cavern. I was intending to wead it after I'd shown Gwunch my idea for his cure, but his tooth made a large hole thwough the pages. Still," he added, "I might ask Gwunch if he has a copy he could lend me. I seem to wecollect it was called 'The Guardian of Health'."

Graffyn returned early the next morning, accompanied by Gyum and the much talked about Wopknocker bird.

"Well, here we are then," said Graffyn, cheerfully. "Sorry I took so long, but if you'll just open wide, Gyum can set his bird to work without further delay."

"What, might I ask, are you talking about?" said Grunch, feigning a look of surprise.

"Your tooth, of course."

"What tooth?"

"Oh, come on, Grunch. Stop stalling, you big coward." Graffyn taunted.

"I'm sorry," replied Grunch, turning to address Gyum, "but it seems you are the unwilling victim of one of Graffyn's pranks. He's well known for this sort of thing in these parts."

Graffyn looked nonplussed.

"I can assure you that I do not require the services of you or your excellent bird."

"'Ere, wot's your game, wizard?" demanded Gyum, angrily.

"What? Me? It's him I tell you; he's got a tooth to come out!" Graffyn pointed wildly to Grunch who was pretending to look bored with the whole affair.

"I ask you, as an expert in these matters," Grunch said, earnestly, "do I look as if I'm in need of a tooth extraction?"

The Wopknocker, which had been staring intently at Grunch's mouth (no doubt, sizing up the job in hand) darted forward, gave him a quick once over and then shook its head emphatically.

"Looks like you was right, dragon. This 'ere wizard 'as bin 'avin fun at me expense, so 'e 'as."

"No! No! This dragon has . . ."

"Listen 'ere," interrupted Gyum, his eyes narrowing and his grey beard bristling at the edges, "me bird don't lie. So, if I don't get payed the price as agreed by you, I'm goin' to let 'im sort the matter out, if you see what I mean."

The Wopknocker leaned slowly forward until it's eyes were level with Graffyn's and its beak rested against the tip of the wizard's nose. Graffyn gulped, kept his mouth tightly shut, and nodded vigorously.

"Good!" pronounced Grunch. "And now we've sorted that out to everyone's satisfaction, I too have a small matter of payment to receive." He handed Graffyn a sheet of parchment.

"Wadsthish?" hissed Graffyn, scarcely daring to open his mouth more than a hair's width.

"Your bill," replied Grunch. "Transport by Hulbert, charged one day at double time." He paused, as if awaiting a query. "You see," he added, "it was his day off and he won't be at all happy if he only gets the normal rate."

"You! . . . You! . . ." Graffyn looked set to explode.

"Careful," warned Grunch, pointing to the Wopknocker, "Remember to keep your mouth closed." The dragon gave a wry smile. "Let's just say we're even."

As Graffyn left Cairn Tor, shadowed by Gyum and the Wopknocker, some of the younger dragons looked up in surprise towards Grunch's cavern, not quite sure they could believe their ears. Grunch was actually laughing!

KOOZL AND THE FLOGGLE

Overnight a heavy dew had fallen, bending the grass and damping the trunks of trees and the smooth, weather-rounded backs of boulders. The perfumed breath of the night had touched and condensed upon all surfaces, leaving a reminder of its passing to endure after the sun had heaved itself clear of the trees on Keldorran's eastern edge and chivvied the darkness into pools of deep shadow where the trees grew thickest.

Two small dragons, who had left the high slopes of Cairn Tor soon after first light and were now in sight of Keldorran's western boundary, halted before the swathe of tawny grass which lay between them and the first trees.

"Lovely! Grazzi, look! Lovely!" cried the smaller of the two, enraptured by the play of golden light diffracted by countless water droplets. "Shiny grass!"

"Wet grass," returned Grazzi, brushing it lightly with a paw. "Too wet to lie down."

"Grazzi not lie down yet," the smallest dragon replied in admonishment. "Koozl want play there!" As he said this he pointed emphatically to the trees.

Grazzi looked horrified. "We can't walk through that. We'll get soaked and you'll catch a chill." He showed his dampened paw to prove his point. "Why don't we have a quick nap here and then, perhaps later, when the sun's dried . . ."

"No! No! Koozl want play there!" insisted the little dragon, before adding in a softer voice: "Then Koozl play quiet and not wake Grazzi. Koozl play long, long time and Grazzi sleep long, long time in warm, warm sun."

"Promise?" asked Grazzi, somewhat sceptically.

"Promise. Koozl play so-oo quiet when Grazzi sleep."

Grazzi looked longingly towards the trees. The air was warming rapidly and, though he detested the idea of pushing through the wet grass, sleeping a 'long, long time in warm, warm sun' sounded like a recipe for the most perfect day imaginable.

"Promise?" he asked again, wanting to make absolutely sure Koozl would keep his side of the bargain.

Koozl made no reply; or if he did, Grazzi did not hear it. Taking the question to be as good as an agreement he plunged headlong into the grass, sending a shower of droplets over his babysitter.

Grazzi looked on, exasperated. Why was he the only young dragon in Cairn Tor to truly appreciate the benefits of sleeping? Everything was pretty much the same when you woke up as it was when you fell asleep, and it seemed a tragic waste of slumber-time to do today what could keep until tomorrow . . . or even the next day. Still, he was wet now.

Much to Grazzi's delight, the journey through the grass was not as discomfiting as he feared it might be. By following closely in Koozl's wake he managed to remain acceptably dry from the belly up and, upon emerging on the other side, he had found everything to be very much to his satisfaction. Koozl had hardly time to take in all the possibilities of exploration this new landscape presented before Grazzi had swept a large mound of dead leaves together with his tail.

"Now don't you forget your promise," he reminded. "I don't want to be woken until the sun is directly above this tree." Grazzi estimated this should equate to at least half a day's sleeping time. He was about to settle into his leaf-bed when he added, "And don't go any further than the third row of trees so I can keep an eye on you."

"Koozl go four trees. Then play very, very quiet."

"Alright; but no further," agreed Grazzi. "Baby dragons who go too far have been known to vanish and never be seen or heard of again," he warned. Grazzi was pleased to see Koozl looking suitably scared. "Now see, I've tied a knot in the end of my tail to remind me about your promise. Play quietly."

With that, Grazzi snuggled deep into his leaf-mattress, put his favourite finger in his mouth, and fell asleep.

Koozl was a good dragonlet. He knew right from wrong, was

rarely selfish, respected the words of his elders and understood that a promise made was a promise that should be kept. He also, like most youngsters, was afraid of the unknown at the same time as being attracted to it — fear and curiosity existing as different sides of the same pebble.

When he began to explore his new surroundings, fear outweighed curiosity. But as time passed with nothing springing out of the shadows to seize him, his fear of the unknown diminished as quickly as his curiosity grew. The sun had barely moved closer to the appointed tree before the first four rows of trees had been explored. True, there were enough thickets, glades and thorn tangles to have occupied him fully, but compared to the lure of the unknown and the promise of the wonders undoubtably awaiting his discovery beyond the fifth, sixth and seventh rank of trees, they seemed insignificant and hardly worth a second glance.

The seventh row became the eighth, the eighth became the ninth, and so on, until Koozl had penetrated so deep into the forest that he moved through a world of green twilight, and the open ground where Grazzi slept appeared as a thin ribbon of pale brightness in the distance. In sight of this, Koozl still felt safe.

But a tree is a tree, a glade is a glade and one thorn bush the same as the next in a forest the size of Keldorran, and soon everything began to appear very similar. Thus Koozl was drawn on, deeper and deeper, and only realised he could no longer see the daylight when the noises began.

At first, he excused half-heard whispering as tricks played by his own imagination. But the whispers became murmurs, and the murmurs grew into strange chatterings which, in turn, gave way to cold, cruel, mocking laughter. Then tiny lights, red and yellow, began to wink and gleam, first here, then there; a flicker, and then gone in the instant the eye caught them. Koozl was frightened. Koozl was lost. Koozl was in terrible danger.

There are those in the Forest of Keldorran who walk the Path of Darkness; bondslaves who wait upon the black desires of N'Borg. Some of their names are known only unto him. Most of their deeds follow his evil design. All of their lives are given over completely to satisfying every whim of his corrupted, festering soul. Without doubt, such were those who now drew closer to Koozl, feeding upon his fear.

Koozl began to run, but always the laughter and the pin-pricks of lights seemed to outstrip him and turn him back. And now, crossing and recrossing the path in front of him, came shapes, made as if from shadows, which owned no recognisable form or size. Time and again he tried to throw flame in the direction of the fleeting shapes, but fear choked him, and only a few sparks issued from his snout, causing the laughter to increase.

Finally, blinded by panic, Koozl ran headlong into a tangle of thorns, fighting and pushing his way through intertwined creepers to the very heart of the bush. Now he was trapped. The laughter surrounded him. The lights danced on all sides. There came the sound of dead leaves crackling underfoot and creepers being pulled aside. Koozl closed his eyes, covered his ears and threw himself towards the ground.

But space, not leaves and earth received him. He was falling. Koozl knew nothing after for a long time.

Koozl returned to consciousness lying flat on his back. At first, he lay perfectly still, then, carefully, he slowly extended each finger in turn. Then he twiched his tail. It was only after he was convinced that he was alive and in one piece that he opened his eyes, fraction by fraction.

He might have kept them closed, so total was the darkness in which he now found himself enveloped. Still he waited, fearing the laughter and the lights would return to resume their taunting game at any moment. But Koozl was alone. Somehow he had eluded their evil clutches and, eventually, he felt it safe enough to sit upright and grope about him in the hope of finding some solid surface beyond the ground beneath him.

When his paws had found nothing in the dark void, panic began to reassert itself, boiling in the pit of his belly and rising up into his throat before issuing as a loud, forlorn sob, accompanied by a handful of sparks.

In the brief instant of illumination before the sparks were engulfed by the darkness, Koozl glimpsed a small, huddled shape lying directly in front of him.

"Who you?" he asked, querulously, his voice sounding small and insignificant as though hardly capable of breaking the heavy silence.

His question solicited no response. No movement. No sound. Nothing. Whatever it was neither ran away nor approached closer.

Koozl attempted to strike up a flame and, this time, succeeded in producing a small, but persistent aura of blue fire about the end of his snout.

The shape had not moved and, somewhat reassured by its apparent lifelessness, the small dragon inched closer, his own light casting gigantic shadow-replicas of himself on a curving wall behind him, Koozl leant slowly forward.

Two ears, two arms, two legs, two eyes . . . two eyes! Koozl nearly extinguished his flame in alarm, but the strange creature made no movement and merely stared up at him, unblinking.

"Me Koozl. Who you?" he asked, trying to control the nervous tremor in his voice.

Still it made no reply.

"Sleep? . . . Dead? . . ." Koozl wondered softly, and cautiously extended an enquiring paw.

When he gently stroked one of the creatures legs it did not, as he had half expected, suddenly spring to life but continued to stare as he proceeded to examine its body, arms and, finally, touched it's head. All the while the strange animal regarded him in what Koozl decided was a friendly sort of way. It was not smooth-scaled like him, but covered in thick fur which was soft to the touch; and, whilst it displayed no outward signs of life, Koozl felt certain that, in some sense, here was a thing capable of feelings and, most importantly, of understanding what was said to it even though it appeared unable to reply on its own account.

At length, Koozl picked it up, brushed it down and cuddled it close, pressing the side of his cheek to the creature's soft face. When he looked, Koozl saw that the creature did not object to being cuddled in the slightest. In fact, Koozl was inclined to think that it had begun to smile appreciatively.

"Friend!" Koozl pronounced, warmly. "Koozl and Friend. Koozl not scared. Friend look after Koozl and Koozl look after Friend! Not scared no more together!"

Carrying Friend carefully in his mouth, Koozl set off, determined to try and find his way back to the safe daylight world where Grazzi slept. In the circle of eerie light cast by his blue flame, he could just make out that he was in some kind of tunnel and, by the hollow sound attending his paw steps and the tree roots latticing the ceiling, he knew it to be both long and underground, running beneath the Forest of Keldorran.

How long he walked, he could not guess, time losing all meaning in a world of no sun, but the effort needed to sustain his flame was increasing, and Koozl knew his internal boiler must be running low on fuel. This would be a serious condition for any dragon in normal circumstances; but for one such as he, lost, and with no idea when he might find suitable food, it was potentially very dangerous indeed. Recognising this, Koozl made a very brave and adult decision. He must extinguish his flame and walk on in darkness, saving his ability to produce light for emergencies only. After stopping to inform Friend that there was no reason to feel afraid, and giving him an especially tight cuddle, Koozl journeyed on in complete darkness.

It is strange how, deprived of one sense, our other senses seem to compensate for the loss, becoming sharper and more acute. So it was for Koozl. He found he almost 'knew' when the tunnel was about to take a turn or sudden slope even before his paws had detected the change. The all-pervading smell of damp earth would, occassionally, carry a tinge of the outside, of the above-ground world of trees and sunlight, and Koozl realised at such points that he must be passing beneath a vertical shaft running up to the surface; too small to climb out of, but all too easy to fall down, as his present situation proved. But it was through his ears that Koozl first detected something amiss.

Passing one of many side-tunnels which branched from the main shaft, Koozl faintly discerned the sound of water, falling from a great height in regular, steady drips. Perhaps this would lead a way out of the subterranean labyrinth? He had just begun to move towards the sound when he detected a sudden change, a slight alteration in the pressure of the static air in the tunnel behind him; as if something now occupied its space like a bung being slowly forced along a tube. Koozl paused. There followed a faint sniffling, snouting sort of sound, then the dry shuffle of large feet disturbing the dust of the tunnel floor. A chill ran the length of Koozl's back to the tip of his tail and up again. Something warned him, that unlike his meeting with Friend, he was in real danger, and that this danger was closing the distance between them. On it came, until Koozl could hear the steady rasp and hiss of its breathing, and the wet, nasal snuffle as it scented him out.

"Quick!"

Koozl started so violently he almost swallowed Friend. Then something clutched his paw tightly and began to drag him roughly down the tunnel so quickly it was difficult to keep his balance. This was followed by a shriek from behind, so terrible it nearly rooted Koozl to the spot with fear.

Miraculously, the whole tunnel now seemed to light up before his unknown ally, almost as brilliantly as day, as if the one who led him carried a powerful lantern.

On they ran, darting down one tunnel, scampering down another, twisting, turning through wide tunnels and narrow, all the while the angry shrieks of their pursuer ringing about them.

Then, just when it seemed he could go no further, the figure before him stopped, dropped something to the ground, then pushed Koozl roughly into the mouth of yet another passageway before scuttling in after him.

"Sshh!" it hissed, its lantern going out. "Quiet, by inky!"

Koozl pulled Friend close to him, burying his face in the warm fur and fighting down the urge to cry out in fear of the unseen terror.

"Sniff! Sniff!" It had stopped running. "Sniff! Sniff!" It crept closer, closer, shuffling towards them until Koozl knew it to be standing barely more than a paw's reach from their hiding place.

"A . . . A . . . A . . . Atchoo!!! A-Atchoo! Atchoo!" Now an angry yowl; then more sneezing; then yowling, shrieking and sneezing all at once.

In the midst of the deafening uproar Koozl felt a firm tug on his paw. When he looked up the narrow tunnel before him was once more filled with light. This time, his guide led the way at a more comfortable pace, away from their sneeze-wracked pursuer. It was only then that Koozl noticed the figure in front of him travelled in a series of long hops, and that the light by which they found their way came not from any lantern, but shone forth from its eyes.

It seemed an age before, having negotiated a particularly confusing network of passages, Koozl was led into a small chamber which seemed little more than a junction where several tunnels came together at the same point. Set into the centre of the arching ceiling, a single, yellow krystal glowed, bathing everything in a soft, restful light.

"Home!" declared Koozl's saviour, spreading his hands expansively and looking extremely proud.

This was Koozl's first opportunity to study his new acquaintance in detail. He was not unlike the drawing of a Shadi-Sampi croakhopper Koozl had seen in a picture book, except larger, about Koozl's own height, and much darker of skin. And whilst the limbs of a croakhopper all ended in webbed feet, his front limbs bore hands, the fingers flattened at their ends and each was furnished with a long, tapering nail. But most remarkable of all were his eyes. These were huge, protruding, circular dishes that stood out, bulging from his head. In the tunnels they had blazed with light, but now, at rest, seemed content to shine with a shimmering silver wash, like twin moons.

"Koo-zul likes Pooter's home?" it prompted, obviously a little disappointed by the dragonlet's lack of enthusiasm.

"Nice home, yes," replied Koozl, politely, whilst thinking quite the opposite. Then realising the creature had called him by name, he asked, "How you know me Koozl?"

Pooter's face broke into a broad toothless grin. "You Koo-zul, him Friend, me Pooter," he replied, pointing to each in turn. "Pooter knows, by inky. Pooter always knows." He laughed, a long, gurgling, liquid laugh.

"How?" persisted Koozl.

"Pooter is seeing when Koo-zul does not see. Pooter is hearing when Koozl is speakificating to Friend. And Pooter knows when Flawgrintawd comes with a sniff and a snuff for to gobbldyup you."

"Who?"

"Flawgrintawd," Pooter hissed, his eyes dimming. "Bad, bad is Flawgrintawd. He came after Koo-zul wanting to gobbldyup, by inky, so he did."

"Koozl and Friend scared of Flaw . . . Fr . . . monster," Koozl admitted.

"So is Pooter, by inky, so I am! Flawgrintawd has gobbldyup all Floggles; mother, father, brothers, sisters all gobbldyup. Only Pooter lives here now, lonelificating, all by himselfing. Pooter hate Flawgrintawd, by inky, I does!" Pooter looked mournful.

"Brave Pooter," said Koozl, in an effort to console him.

"No! No!" Pooter denied vigorously. "Pooter is scaredyscuttled out of his skin. But Pooter sees and Flawgrintawd does not. He can only sniffticate and snufflyfum." He performed a brief mime of Flawgrintawd's hunting methods, closing his eyes and shuffling across the floor, arms outstretched, stopping frequently to sniff loudly. "But Pooter is cleverish too," he continued, sounding brighter. "I fixicates him good, by inky, I does. I puts this in fronts of him," he said, showing Koozl a powder resembling fine sand, "Then he sneezes fit to bursticome and I hears him coming to gobbldyup."

"Pooter clever," Koozl agreed.

"Never close before I hears him," Pooter confirmed. "Excepticating now. That was nearly gobblydyup, by inky, it was! Phew!" Pooter made his eyes blaze and rolled them so far back into their sockets it seemed they performed a complete revolution.

"How do that?" enquired Koozl, fascinated.

"What?"

"Make eyes fire."

"Oh, that," replied Pooter, nonchalantly. "S'easy for Floggles. We consumerates spangle roots, lots and lots."

"Taste nice?" Koozl was feeling suddenly peckish.

"What! I'll say, by inky! Scrumpticiousness!" Pooter shot a long tongue out of one side of his mouth. "Wanting to try?"

Koozl nodded. "Friend too," he said, remembering his silent companion.

"And Friend. Comefollow, but careful beforelisten Flawgrintawd," he warned.

"By inky, yes!" replied Koozl.

"Yes, by inky!" laughed Pooter, hopping away down one of the tunnels, his eyes once more lighting their way.

Much to Koozl's dismay, he found it impossible to share Pooter's enthusiasm for spangle roots. Whilst Pooter, who had snapped off several which hung down from a low ceiling, set about them with obvious relish, Koozl sat with his snout hidden in Friend's furry belly. The smell was awful, and the fumes which the noxious roots gave off when broken were so strong they made his eyes water. Despite Pooter's invitations to 'gobbldyup', Koozl could not bring himself to come within a tail's length of a single root, let alone put one in his mouth and chew it. He found it difficult to comprehend how, or why, Flawgrintawd should want to eat any Floggle which stuffed itself so full of foul-smelling food.

"Not like?" asked Pooter.

"Yuk! No!" replied Koozl, Friend still pressed to his nostrils. "Then comefollow againly," the Floggle said, swallowing the last root. "I'm knowing something ever bettering than spangle root, by inky, yes I am. The specialist of everyall floggle food. Koo-zul will surehappy like it."

This time Pooter led Koozl to a length of tunnel where the earth appeared permanently damp and, by the frequent piles of fresh soil against the walls, liable to collapse. Here and there, puddles of stagnant water glimmered and gleamed, reflecting the light from Pooter's eyes.

"Being quiet now you must," cautioned Pooter, holding up a finger to his mouth, "or they'll be hearing us, by inky, and I shan't be able to extracticate them."

"Who they?" enquired Koozl.

"Jubbers," he hissed. "Lovelyjuice jubbers for Koo-zul and Pooter."

"And Friend."

"Friend too if he's hungrying. Now be quietness and watch."

Pooter moved along the walls, pressing the side of his face to the wet soil, listening. This continued for some time before his eyes suddenly flashed bright.

"I'm hearing some here!" he whispered, excitedly. "Five, six or even sevenses and nonmistake!"

He began tapping lightly with the flattened ends of his fingers upon the soil, slowly at first, but quickening, faster and faster until the air was filled with the sound of drumming fingers and Pooter appeared to be performing some strange dance, weaving side to side and bobbing up and down.

"Comequick!" he urged, his voice tense with excitement. "The jubbers are outcoming. Be grabbing them, quickascanly, when they drops."

Koozl darted forward to stand close to Pooter who continued drumming. The dragonlet was unsure what a jubber looked like or how he was meant to catch them, but he was determined to show willingness to help.

"Here they comes!" croaked Pooter, his eyes concentrating on the wall. "Ready getting Koo-zul, here they comes!"

Koozl stared in disbelief at the wall beneath Pooter's hands. Where, moments before, soil and roots existed, there was now a seething, writhing mass of serpentile forms. One of the jubbers suddenly fell from the wall and dropped at Koozl's feet, coiling itself around his leg.

Quicker than blinking, Pooter's enormous tongue flicked out and fastened around Koozl's tail.

"I've gottim! By inky, Pooter's gottim!"

'No! No! Koozl's tail not jubber!" Koozl protested indignantly. "Pooter let go!"

"Sorryness," Pooter apologized, freeing Koozl's tail and instantly wrapping his tongue around the flailing jubber. Then, to Koozl's distaste, he sucked it in and began to swallow greedily, the ends of the jubber protruding from the corners of his mouth and looking like an animated pink moustache.

"Uggh!" Koozl wrinkled his face.

"Yumminy-yum!" said Pooter, appreciatively, the jubber vanishing in a gulp. "Koo-zul try now," he urged, digging his fingers into another writhing body which was still half embedded in the wall and tugging furiously.

"No. Koozl want find Grazzi now. Pooter take Koozl there."

Pooter continued his tug-o-war contest with the stubborn jubber. "Grat-zee?"

"Yes. Grazzi up there," said Koozl, pointed to the ceiling. "He waiting for Koozl."

"Badplace. Noisysome. Koo-zul stay with Pooter and be consumification jubbers, by inky!"

"Koozl home there! Pooter take Koozl!" Koozl looked as though he might cry.

Distracted by Koozl's demand, Pooter slackened his grip

slightly on the jubber. With a sudden convulsive twist it shook free and vanished into the wall with an audible 'ploop!'.

"Oh, mudbuckets!" cursed Pooter. "The jubber's escapified now!" He looked a little annoyed. "Alrighting," he conceded, "comefollow againly." He hopped past Koozl, muttering under his breath. "Don't like spangle root! Don't like jubber! By inky, Koo-zul is a sillyfication and nonmistake!

'Where Grat-zee be? In tree upstairs?" asked Pooter, once he had regained something of his former good humour.

"No. Grazzi wait close to trees for Koozl."

"Hmm. Difficulty that way. Pooter does not go for there now. Must go thoroughly very small ways, then big ways, then where Flawgrintawd home is: dangerous then. By inky, dangerous. Why doesn't Koo-zul stay with Pooter? I'll discovericate roots that Koo-zul be muchlikeingness."

"No. Koozl's family up there," Koozl replied.

"Ahh, family. Yes. Nicelytimes for Pooter when he had family, before Flawgrintawd . . ." Pooter looked mournful again, wiped the corner of his eyes with a finger, and hopped on. "Comefollow. Pooter will make Koo-zul sure happy and find Grat-zee, by inky, I will."

So Pooter led Koozl on, through the matrix of tunnels where no daylight ever comes; through wide tunnels and narrow; straight tunnels and winding; tunnels which sloped up and ones which sloped down. The Floggle stopped frequently to listen and shine his light behind them, ever alert for the stealthy approach of Flawgrintawd.

It was after they had travelled for some time along a tunnel of exceeding girth that Pooter stopped and motioned to Koozl that they must now proceed with extreme caution.

"Just alongways here is Flawgrintawd's home. Try not to be speakificating," he whispered, before hopping on ahead.

The monotony of the tunnel system Koozl had seen thus far had not prepared him for the sight which followed. Close behind Pooter, he emerged into a vast chamber, larger than the great Assembly Hall at Cairn Tor. And, not only did it differ in scale from the rest of Pooter's underground world, here, much to Koozl's delight, the cavern seemed afire with the brilliance shining from countless krystals of every shape and hue imaginable!

"Flawgrintawd home," spat Pooter, distastefully. "Horrid. All this lightness makes my eyes go burning sore. Bad, bad place and nonmistaking. Look . . ."

Koozl looked, lying upon the floor directly before them was a heap of bones, twice Koozl's height, white and age-polished, glowing eerily in the false daylight.

"All of Flawgrintawd's gobbldyups there," hissed Pooter. "Pooter's family is surelything with them." He studied the pile, looking to see if he could discern the remains of a now extinct relation.

Koozl's attention was soon distracted by other sights. All about the cavern were scattered various objects, most of them unfamiliar. To one side a pile of books, their pages mouldered and decaying. To another, a square, box-shaped object constructed entirely from wood, one facet of which mirrored the krystal-light like a sheet of green ice. In the centre of the cavern, a table, also of wood, and upon it another wooden box inset with a patch of lattice work surrounded by several circular knobs. Three or four wooden chairs stood around the table and, directly beneath the legs of one, a creature, similar in appearance to Friend, but much smaller and more brightly coloured, lay face down. Without knowing why, Koozl felt an overwhelming sadness.

"What all these things?" he asked. "Belong monster?"

Pooter shook his head. "No. Always here before Flawgrintawd, before Floggles. Beforetimes everything I'm thinking. Now, quietness, comefollow," he instructed, ushering Koozl into yet another tunnel.

Not long after leaving the cavern of Flawgrintawd they entered a tunnel system where the quality of air underwent a sudden and very noticeable change. Instead of the static, heavy

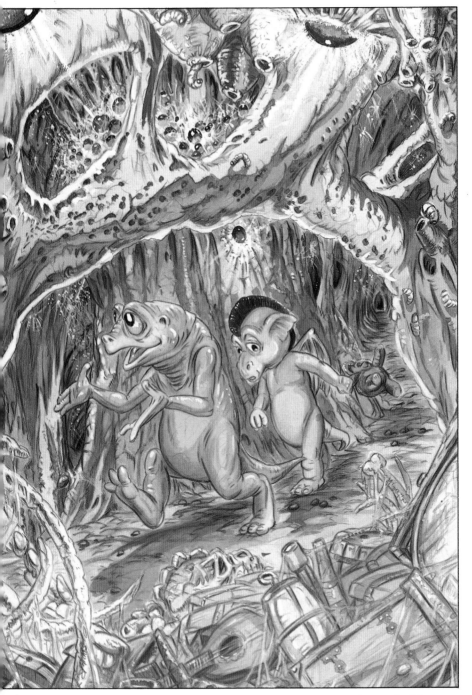

...ed by Pooter the Floggle, Koozl and friend journey through the underground labyrinth of the ...rrible Flawgrintawd.

atmosphere Koozl had become accustomed to, the air in these tunnels seemed lighter, fresher, and slightly turbulent. Even before Pooter told him, even before he saw daylight glimmering in the distance, Koozl knew he was approaching journey's end.

"I'm no furthergoing now," said Pooter. "Too hurting for my eyes up there. Koo-zul can find upstairs from here."

"Pooter come and see Grazzi."

"Impossification," Pooter replied. "Floggles hate upstairs. Only sometimes go when big light gone and all small lights are outcoming. Not now, much too hurting for my eyes it is. Koo-zul go finding Grat-zee and then getmusting Koo-zul food. Go now with bestluckily."

"Koozl thank Pooter. Friend thank Pooter. Pooter is good, good Floggle. Pooter is best, best Floggle!" Koozl rushed forward and embraced Pooter tightly.

"By inky! Oh, by inky!" exclaimed Pooter. "Pooter is liking Koo-zul muchly too."

"And Friend?"

"Of coursely, and Friend," Pooter laughed. "Now Koo-zul mustly go."

"Koozl will bring Grazzi and other dragons to see Pooter soon," Koozl promised.

"No," replied Pooter sternly. "Upstairs bad, bad place for Floggles but downstairs bad, bad place for Koo-zuls. Koo-zul must stay with Grat-zee and all family and not leave againly. Next time Pooter mightly not see beforetime Flawgrintawd gobbldyups. Understandificate?"

"Yes, by inky," Koozl said, grinning. "Pooter be careful and see monster quick."

"Don't worryoube. I'll be alrightly." He waved and hopped off, swallowed almost immediately by the darkness.

Koozl found Grazzi without much difficulty, having emerged from beneath a bush within sight of his leaf-bed. Grazzi was sound asleep, snoring like a nest of stinglers and, much to

Koozl's relief, the sun was only just approaching its zenith above the tree when he ran up and tugged several times on Grazzi's tail.

"Leave me alone and go play," mumbled Grazzi, without opening his eyes.

"Time for home. Koozl hungry now," persisted Koozl, shaking Grazzi's tail vigorously.

"Dear me," Grazzi grumbled, stretching and blinking, "I can't ever get a moment's peace and quiet. Here I've been, lying out in the hot sun while you've been enjoying yourself, and no sooner do I close my eyes for a quick nap than you come pestering me to go home!"

"Comefollow, by inky," said Koozl.

"What gibberish is that?" retorted Grazzi, now wide awake. "Really, Koozl, it's about time you began to talk properly. It's hard to understand you at times." The dragon dusted the leaves from his flanks and began to walk towards the grass. "What's that?" he asked, noticing Friend for the first time.

"Friend," said Koozl, proudly. "Koozl find him."

"Hmm. Well, he looks the worse for wear if you ask me. He's filthy, looks like he's been buried alive. Come to that," continued Grazzi, adopting a superior air, "So do you."

"Friend help Koozl," replied the dragonlet, quick to defend his accomplice's reputation. "Koozl help Friend. Pooter help Koozl and Friend. Flaw . . . Flaw . . . monster chase Koozl then Pooter helps. Underground Koozl goes. See spangle root, jubbers, krystal, lots and lots Koozl sees. Then Koozl . . ."

"Quiet!" Grazzi commanded, holding up a paw . . . "Honestly, you're giving me a headache. It sounds as if you've been dreaming, not me. Now let's pretend to be grown up dragons, shall we, and talk about something sensible. I know, if you like I'll tell you about the time I slept for four days in a row and everyone thought I was dead . . ."

The two dragons began to head back towards Cairn Tor, where dinner was waiting, the older one talking, the younger one listening.

"You see what I mean about sleeping," said Grazzi. "Everything's the same when you wake up."

Koozl said nothing. He simply smiled to himself, gave Friend a squeeze, and noticed how dry the grass was.

ALL IN A NIGHT'S WORK

The end of the Season of Harvest is a time for remembering. Then, it seems Krystonia holds its breath: a brief interlude between the long hot days when the crops grow to fullness, and the endless, bone-chilling nights of a winter soon to come, when all Krystonia sleeps, bound in ice, until the Reawakening sets the land free once more.

Within this brief span of precious days, when the weather is neither too hot nor too cool, representatives of all races journey to an appointed meeting place in order to join the celebration of Gron-Hayha — The Great Joy.

For four days and four nights old friendships are rekindled, new ones forged, and petty disputes forgotten in an endless round of feasting, singing and dancing. Each time a different race is chosen to host the festivities and, whilst no guest would ever be so ill-mannered as to suggest a Gron-Hayha had been a flop, there can be little doubt that the hosts of a successful celebration gain a certain amount of respect and notoriety which may stand them in good stead when conducting business.

So, this account concerns one such time — the Gron-Hayha of Cairn Tor.

Stoope was depressed. Earlier that same day Grunch had called to ask if preparations for the final night's entertainment were well advanced.

"Just a few minor details, some fine-tuning is needed, and all will be ready," Stoope had lied. "Oh, yes, I believe that this will be a show to end all shows!" He said this so enthusiastically he almost convinced himself it was true.

"It had better be," warned Grunch, "or you'll be wishing you really could disappear!"

Shadra happened to be passing by when she noticed Stoope,

obviously distressed, huddled in the shadows of a rocky overhang. He was conspicuously trying to be inconspicuous.

"What's up, Stoopey?" she enquired.

"What's up! What's up! I'll tell you what's up, Grunch is going to skin me alive come the end of Harvest! Take a good look, go on, this is how I want to be remembered; all in one piece with my hide still covering my bones! Oh, the tragedy! What a waste! A great artiste doomed to die!" He held his tail to his forehead and effected a graceful, though badly over-acted swoon.

"Dear me, you are in a bad way," said Shadra, though quite used to Stoope's theatrics. "Why should Grunch want to skin you?"

"Gron-Hayha," he replied, his eyes still closed. "Or, should I say, Groan-Hayha."

"I still don't understand. I thought Gron-Hayha was a time for rejoicing, not blubbering?"

"It is! It is! That's the whole problem. I've told Grunch I've got the show for the Grand Finale all arranged. I haven't. I don't have the faintest idea of what to do!"

"What's wrong with your magic act and the flamethrowing? That always goes down . . . err . . . consistently," she consoled.

"There you are, you see. You've said it. Always! Always! I've been performing that act for ages and, as mind-bogglingly brilliant as it is, I'll get stoned off the stage if I do it again. Especially for the Grand Finale!"

"So, do something different," replied Shadra, simply.

"Different! Different she says!" Stoope exclaimed. "My dear girl, you cannot possibly know what it is like to be a famous performer. You don't just get up and *do* something! It takes time and practice to perfect an act. Even if I could think of something new — which I can't — there's nowhere near enough time to rehearse." He exploded into a fit of uncontrolled wailing, punctuated with descriptions of the various useful objects Grunch would soon be making from his hide.

"That is enough!" scolded Shadra, adopting the tone of a female dragon chastising a naughty dragonlet. "Honestly, I would have expected more professionalism from someone calling himself Stoope the Stoopendous!"

"Professionalism!" replied Stoope, collecting himself. "She's telling me, the great Stoope, about professionalism? Why, my girl, they invented the word 'professionalism' to describe me!"

"Well let's see some of it then. If you pull yourself together I might have a solution to get you out of this mess."

"You! Help? Why, do you know a good hiding place?"

"No. I know where we can find everything to put on a good . . . a brilliant show."

"Where?" asked Stoope, doubtfully.

"Right here, in Cairn Tor."

Shadra's idea rested upon the various talents of the younger dragons. True, she had to concede that they were completely inexperienced troubadors, but they were enthusiastic and, potentially, entertainers par excellence.

"That lot!" Stoope exclaimed. "Do you comprehend the meaning of talent? When I think of the stresses and strains placed upon the performer, treading the dusty cavern floor alone, the attentions of thousands fixed upon his every word and gesture. The roar of the granite-dust makeup! The smell of the crowd!"

"The *roar* of the crowd," corrected Shadra.

"Whatever," replied Stoope, working himself up into a monologue. "There I stand, the audience enthralled, and I deliver my lines . . ."

"Keep quiet!" snapped Shadra. "This is getting us nowhere. Now, I think they'll be brilliant. Believe me, they'll cause a storm!"

"A thunderstorm!" snorted Stoope, uncharitably.

"All they need," she continued, ignoring Stoope's jibe, "is a bit of practice. Maybe a dress rehearsal or two. And, most importantly, a good publicity campaign."

"My career! My reputation!" wailed Stoope. "Placed in the paws of infants!"

"Your hide," Shadra reminded. "Now, do you agree to give them a chance?"

"Though the Great Gadzoot, wherever he finally vanished to, would spin on the spot to hear me say it, yes, I agree."

"Good!" concluded Shadra. "I'll get back to you when I've discussed the matter with the performers."

"I think," objected Stoope, "as resident theatrical genius of Cairn Tor, that it is I who should audition the cast."

"In good time," Shadra replied. "All in good time."

The first Stoope knew about his self-appointed publicity agent's actions was when large, brightly coloured sheets of parchment began to appear on boulders, trees, buildings and anything else which remained motionless long enough to be posted. Even several walls of The Obelisk bore the posters proclaiming:

CAIRN TOR PRODUCTIONS
PROUDLY PRESENTS

THE
GRON-HAYHA
EXTRAVAGANZA!

FEATURING
DOCTOR PULTZR THE AMAZING
MEMORY-DRAGON
_____

SCREAMIN' SPYKE AND THE
ADOLESCENTS
_____

THE ONE AND ONLY
JUMBLY
THE JUGGLER
_____

AND THE MOST SPECTACULAR
FANTASIA OF FLAME

YOUR ARTISTIC DIRECTOR:
STOOPE GRUMBLYPEG

"So!" said Grunch, holding one of the posters accusingly under Stoope's snout, "This is what you call a show to end all shows, is it?"

Stoope smiled weakly, then gulped.

"Well, at least you haven't given yourself top-billing for a change," Grunch observed.

"Yes, my name might appear in larger letters," Stoope commented. "But ... but ..." he continued, changing the subject when he noticed Grunch's quizzical glance, "I'm a great believer in encouraging young talent. Wait until you see what they can do!"

"And? ..."

"What?"

"What exactly *can* they do?" asked Grunch, suspiciously.

"Err ... dear Grunch ... err ... you should know me well enough by now to know that I cannot, nay, will not, break a confidence with my fellow artistes. All I can say is you will have to wait and see. I can promise, you *will* be surprised."

"Nothing compared to the surprise I'll have for you if it goes wrong!" threatened Grunch.

"You obviously aren't satisfied with me being skinned alive!" shouted Stoope, as soon as he found Shadra. "Now you want me boiled at dawn in hot lava!"

"Hush, you'll upset the cast," replied Shadra, calmly. "As you should know, it's not easy handling the artistic temperament."

"It's not going to be easy for me to part with my hide!" exclaimed Stoope, not the least comforted. "What's all this 'Memory-dragon' and 'Fantasia of Flame' rubbish? More to the point, why's my name only in small print at the bottom and not in it's rightful place at the top?"

"Stop worrying. I've got everything under control. And even if your name is in small print it's being read from here to the Waste of Shugg which, you must admit, is something of an improvement."

"The Waste of Shugg, you say?" Stoope looked pleased, then added, "I hope that won't attract an undesirable element. I can't abide hecklers."

"As the Great Gadzoot once said: 'It'll be alright on the night'."

"How d'you know what the Great Gadzoot said? He vanished long before you were out-of-egg."

...w can anyone be expected to concentrate on Flayla's story with Jumbly practicing his ...ling act!

"You always say it," sniggered Shadra.

"I also said I'd never work with furry animals or infants. Now look at me! The Stoopendous Stoope has sunk to this!"

"Stop complaining and come with me," said Shadra. "We've got a lot still to do."

Picture the scene if you will. For four days and three nights Cairn Tor resounded to the sound of record crowds. There was not a cave, not a crevice offering the meanest shelter which was not occupied by the cultural pilgrims of all races. And it had gone well. Grunch, an example of organizational ability, had pulled out all the stops. Everyone was fed. Everyone was happy. And everywhere the greeting of 'Hayha!' was said with enthusiasm and sincerity. All it needed, on this final night, to ensure this Gron-Hayha was voted the most successful ever, was for the evening's entertainment to live up to expectations. In the event, it was a show I and everyone else who witnessed it, will never forget.

The whole of the great cavern was filled with a soft wash of golden light, emanating from several strategically placed krystals which Poffles and Trumph, those most mischevious of Bobolls, had 'borrowed' for Shadra from the hoard of Myzer. Then, unseen by the crowd, one of the more competent Apprentices, whom Shadra had succeeded in charming, made a slight motion with his hands, murmured several spell-words, and caused all the krystals, with the exception of those lighting the stage, to dim simultaneously. This sudden change was greeted with a buzz of expectation, followed by complete silence.

"Welcome one and welcome all to the show to end all shows!" Stoope's voice rang out clear and authorative as he strode dramatically onto the centre of the stage. "It gives me the greatest pleasure to present to you, honoured guests of Cairn

Tor, a treat of talent! An extravanganza of entertainment! A fountain of fun!"

The crowd responded enthusiastically to Stoope's introduction with whistles, cheers, claps and slapping of tails. Stoope help up his paws for silence, obviously revelling in the attention.

"It is at great personal expense that I, Stoope the Stoopendous, have scoured these lands in order to bring you a show almost as good as my One Dragon Show." He paused to allow the audience an opportunity to applaud. They responded, but less vigorously. "Yes, I know many of you will be disappointed that I have decided to forsake centre stage to give others their chance to build a reputation. Tonight, my role will be a small one . . ."

"Unlike your head!" someone shouted. This was greeted by a general round of laughter.

Undaunted, Stoope pressed on. "For many seasons you have looked up to me as one at the pinnacle of his profession . . ."

"What's Stoopey doin'?" hissed Spyke, hidden off stage. "This isn't in the script!"

"I know!" Shadra replied, sternly.

". . . and have asked me, many times, what is it that makes the difference between a mere performer and a great artiste. As I have always replied . . ."

"It's knowing when to get off!" Shadra shouted.

The audience hooted with mirth, certain that Shadra's retort had been a rehearsed joke. Thankfully, Stoope was enough of an entertainer to realise he had overstayed his welcome and, after joining with the laughter himself, proclaimed grandly: "Please give a warm welcome to our first guest — the one and only Doctor Pultzr, the A-mazing Memory-Dragon!"

A roll of log drums, a puff of smoke, and Pultzr appeared on stage clad in a high-collared robe and a wizard's hat which, even before the applause attending his arrival had died away, fell down across his eyes and effectively blindfolded him. Shadra, a small choker of sparkling mirror-shells about her neck, dashed from the wings, whisked the hat from Pultzr's head, executed a graceful curtsy, and dashed off again.

Pultzr looked extremely relieved. Then, opening his wings so that the robe spread impressively, he addressed the audience. "What you are about to witness involves no magic, twickewy, or illusion. It is merely a demonstwation of bwain-power which could be performed by anyone."

"Except a Trolle!" shouted a voice from the middle of the hall. The audience, somewhat impolitely, fell about and, the Trolles, hearing themselves mentioned, began to applaud with enthusiasm.

"Including a Trolle!" Pultzr corrected, at once quieting the crowd. "It is weally a matter of complete concentwation."

For all Pultzr's assurances that anyone could duplicate the feats of memory he performed, I do not believe any member of the audience or, for that matter, anyone, anywhere in Krystonia, could have emulated the little dragon.

After calling upon several volunteers, he proceeded to recite word-perfectly, the first three sentences appearing on any page of their choosing, from any one of several different books. Then, after the most cursory of glances at a tray upon which a variety of small objects, collected at random from members of the audience, were placed, he proceeded to list them all, without a single omission, and correctly identified the owner of each. Finally, he persuaded a whole row of Apprentices to join him on stage. He stood them in a line, gave each a numbered card by which they might be identified and, turning his back so that he was unable to see, allowed them to change places. Pultzr correctly identified each by number — even spotting the deliberate attempt by two Apprentices who swapped cards in the hope of confusing him — and returned them all to their original positions.

It was a display which left everyone *except* the Trolles feeling a little inferior, and lent credibility to the dragons' reputation for being among the wisest of races. Pultzr left the stage, much to Shadra's delight and his amazement, to thunderous applause.

Stoope reappeared, bowed low and smiled. "There, what did I tell you!" he beamed. "To think, when Pultzr first came to me, I said ..." He caught Shadra giving him a dangerous look from the side of the stage and changed direction immediately. "I said, everyone has at least one talent, and none more than our next guests. Please give a rip-roaring Cairn Tor welcome for those musical maestro's, Screamin' Spyke and the Ad-o-lescents!"

The audience applauded, all save for Grunch who, seated at the back of the hall, stuck his fingers in his ears. "Oh no! Don't do this! Not Spyke!" he begged.

The log drums thundered, the stage was enveloped in a cloud of smoke shot through with thin beams of coloured krystal-light, and Spyke, his mane dyed a flambouyant green, bounced onto the stage, the lute of a wandering musician slung carelessly about his neck. He was followed by a self-conscious Owhey and several other youngers, all bearing instruments, and all sporting the same shocking-green manes.

"Yo, kiddos!" Spyke hollered. "Sorry we've lost our drummer, but Grazzi is such a laid-back dude, he fell asleep. So, we'll just have to do our outrageous best without him." Spyke strutted from side to side of the stage, saluting members of the audience. "Our first number is entitled 'Dragon's Love Rock'. Hope it freaks you." Slinging the lute just above his knees, Spyke turned to the Adolescents. "One, two, three, hit it!"

The 'music' was loud. *Very* loud. Deafening, in fact. However, this had one major benefit. Though it was obvious Spyke was belting out his lyrics at the top of his voice, every last word was lost in the wall of sound generated by the Adolescents; and he gyrated, twisted, pouted and strutted through the entire set completely unheard. The music was, surprisingly, quite invigorating in a peculiar way, and, visually, Spyke was, by his own description after the show, 'so hot he was molten!' Before long, every youngster in the hall — along with one or two 'switched-on oldsters', to use another Spyke term — were on their feet and dancing.

As the band played, the krystals pulsed and changed colour

in time to the music, and flames, undoubtably provided by Stoope, flashed across the stage. Regardless of musical tastes, it was a visual experience that saw the band leave the stage to cries of "More! More! More!"

Grunch now sat, open-mouthed, shaking his head in disbelief. "They liked him! They *actually* enjoyed Spyke's music!"

Though the show did much for Spyke's popularity with Krystonia's youth, the next act saw the first performance of a young dragon who had since become a favourite with all ages — Jumbly the Juggling Dragon.

Jumbly juggled rocks and stones of various sizes. He juggled standing on one leg. He juggled with one paw. Then with his tail. He even juggled standing on his head and lying on his back. Then he juggled with everything, at the same time as balancing three stones on the end of his snout. To cap it all, he took eight baby Bobolls from the audience and, whilst their mothers looked on aghast, juggled them as well, keeping all in the air at once!

When Jumbly left the stage, the audience rose as one and applauded so loudly that Grunch feared they might cause a roof-fall. And they refused to stop until Jumbly returned and repeated his trick with the baby Bobolls all over again! Before he left the stage for the second time, Stoope had a contract ready and waiting for his paw-print and had already taken several advance bookings.

The finale, billed as a 'Fantasia of Flame', proved to be a fitting conclusion to such an exciting show. With the hall plunged into darkness, Stoope began by shooting long bolts of rainbowed flame. Then, the whole of the cavern's high roof appeared to split assunder to reveal a confusion of light and colour. Thanks to Pultzr's recently-perfected exploding powder, stars of red, yellow and blue cascaded down before bursting into flame-flowers just above the heads of the spellbound crowd. Lances of light rocketed from the back of the hall, accompanied by loud bangs, pops and screeches, to explode on the stage at Stoope's feet. On the stage itself, fountains of sparks erupted like small volcanoes, gushing upwards before drifting slowly down around Stoope's head. As the dragon bowed low, a huge explosion rocked the crowd, followed by a puff of green smoke, and Stoope vanished. Slowly, the krystals around the hall returned the audience to light and signalled the show's end.

Grunch could not have wished for a better response. Everyone stomped, clapped and cheered as the performers came back onto the stage and took a well deserved bow — Stoope trying to conceal the bandage which was now covering a scorched section of his tail. It had, without doubt, been a show to end all shows and the appropriate ending to the best Gron-Hayha ever. Only the speech of appreciation, to thank the hosts for their hospitality, remained.

To this end, Shigger, Chieftain of the tribes of Maj-Dron, was helped onto the stage.

After thanking Grunch and all dragons generally, he turned to the performers who had retreated to the back of the stage to listen politely.

"In recognition of one of the most entertaining evenings I can recollect, I wish you to accept this small gift as a token of friendship and gratitude." He held out a krystal pendant of such design and quality that only the hands of a Maj-Dron Smith could have crafted it. "The power of the krystal will protect you in all your endeavours," he explained.

As Artistic Director, Stoope stepped forward and accepted graciously, to another round of applause. After waiting for silence, he cleared his throat, but instead of the colourful speech everyone expected, he simply said, "Thank you. It was all in a night's work."

But this story is not yet ended, not quite. The krystal pendant was given later, at a private meeting in Grunch's cavern, to Shadra, along with a good deal of uncustomary praise from Grunch and an equal amount of gratitude from Stoope who, apart from his scorched tail, retained his hide intact thanks to her efforts.

"The ability to work and do good for others, without thought of any reward, is a talent which all possess but too few use," said Grunch, approvingly. "From what I've seen, I shouldn't be at all surprised if Cairn Tor doesn't have a female leader someday." Then, noticing Stoope's look of complete disbelief, he added: "But don't quote me."

From that day to this, Shadra has never been seen without the pendant about her neck. It is, not surprisingly, the most treasured of all her possessions and she would not exchange a single link of it for all the charcoal cookies in Krystonia. There is nothing she will ever own which will be so dear to her.

Except, perhaps, a kiss from Pultzr.

WINGS ARE WONDEROUS THINGS

This evening, after the birds which occupy the hollowed upper branches of my keldorr had returned to roost, I sat awhile on my doorstep watching the sun diminish to a smouldering globe. Already the skinwings were out, swooping and circling beneath the branches as they harried flying insects, their high-pitched constant squeaks punctuated from time to time by the voices of other night creatures who were beginning their moonlit forays through the forest. Then, high above the trees, cutting through the half-light of dusk, a solitary dragon came a-flying.

I watched it drifting silently homeward, the only flicker of movement and life in the vast, dumb eternity of the darkening sky until, far on the horizon, it passed directly across the face of the sun. In that brief instant, when the great beast seemed transformed into a black, perfect silhouette framed by the burning sphere, I felt as though all time, all life existed only in its flight, and I envied the dragon its wings.

What is it to belong to the sky and look down, alone, upon this world? What thoughts belong to a dragon's mind, what sights to its eye, in such moments? What travellers, their limbs aching with the fatigue of the day's journey, up hill and down, looked up from their campfires and wished the effortless glide, beneath which all is levelled, could be theirs?

Our birth fates us never to know; we are bystanders, dreamers who may only imagine and wonder. Yet ours is the comfort of certainty, the knowledge that we shall never yearn long for that which lies beyond our capabilities. But think of the suffering, the frustration of one born with wings who comes to believe he will never fly. This is what Owhey once thought: though when he now comes hurtling through an open shutter and crash-lands on my desk, I sometimes wish it has been truly so. Only sometimes . . .

And so I begin the tale of how Owhey, the most inoffensive of little dragons, finally took to the air. I believe, as so many of my chronicles seem to show, that there is a lesson here we might learn . . .

"Stop worrying; of course you'll be able to fly. I've taught more dragonlets than I can count and they've all got the knack in the end. You're a late developer, that's all."

Groosh was doing his best to allay Owhey's fears. For the last three days he had tried every trick he knew to get the dragonlet airborne and still seemed no closer to success than when training had first begun. Owhey's wings, though only recently out of their protective wing-buds and far from their final span, were sufficiently developed to have allowed a short flight. Yet every attempt so far — and there had been many — had seen Owhey drop like a stone onto the mattresses of sponge-plant without having shown the slightest hint of lift.

"Let's leave it a couple of days to give your wings a rest before we try again," Groosh concluded, seeing Owhey was all but exhausted. "If you feel fit enough, you can practice those wing-strengthening exercises I showed you; but don't overdo them."

Even Flayla, usually guaranteed to offer some sympathy, seemed dismissive when Owhey told her of his problem.

"The trouble with you," she said, without looking up from the picture book she was showing to another dragonlet, "is that you're trying to fly before you can run." She turned a page, pointed out something of interest, then continued: "If Groosh says you'll fly, you'll fly. Goodness, if he doesn't know about such things, who does? You'll see, give it a few more days and you'll be flapping about our heads and causing a right nuisance. Then you'll see it was all a big fuss about nothing. Now run along and practice your exercises."

Owhey did practice. He practiced so hard he woke himself up in the night flapping like a demented skinwing. And when he managed to get back to sleep, he dreamt about flying, seeing himself cutting a graceful figure through the skies of Cairn Tor. Unfortunately, at some point he always remembered he couldn't fly and found himself nose-diving, out of control, down towards jagged rocks. Then he would wake again, shaking with fright, just before he was dashed to pieces.

Subsequent coaching lessons from Groosh only served to heighten Owhey's despair and increase the frequency of his nightmares. He ran, he leapt, he crashed, again and again, until he was bruised all over and was convinced he was the only one willing to admit the awful truth — he was destined for a strictly terrestrial future.

Grunch, overhearing him complaining to Jumbly, patted him on the head and said cryptically, "None decides when a leaf shall fall, but fall it surely will."

Owhey failed to see how Grunch's comment had any bearing in his case, except for the bit about falling. By now he felt he knew, more than most, even leaves, about falling!

Reawakening gave way to the season of Growth and still, apart from the brief interim between takeoff and crash landing, Owhey's feet stayed firmly on the ground. Dragons younger than he were already showing more advanced flying skills on the nursery slope. Owhey was growing desperate; and the more upset he became the less inclined he was to risk another futile attempt with so many onlookers to witness his shortcomings as an aeronaut.

As his confidence evaporated, his attendance at Groosh's flying classes suffered, until Owhey stopped turning up at all and, instead, sat alone trying his best to keep from crying. He was torn between extreme desolation, and anger directed at the useless wings which pointed proudly from his back. Eventually, the situation deteriorated to a point where Groosh felt he had no alternative than to speak to Grunch.

"Does it really matter?" asked Grunch. "After all, I don't fly and I can't say it's ever bothered me."

"Because you didn't come out-of-egg with wings," responded Groosh. "Imagine what you'd feel like if you couldn't make flame. It's the same thing."

"Hmm. I suppose so." Grunch thought for a few moments. "I can't see how I can help, though. You're the flying expert around here."

"I was wondering if you could give me permission to go and speak to Rueggan. I've heard he's experimenting with a flying machine at the moment and hoped, perhaps, he might offer some advice."

"Pah!" snorted Grunch. "What can a wizard tell a dragon about flying? That's like me telling a Trolle how to dig a hole."

"Maybe we need a different approach. You see, I don't think Owhey's problem is physical so much as it's . . . well, 'boulders get bigger until you lift them', as they say."

"Who says?"

"You, for a start."

"Do I? Hmm . . . I quite like that." Grunch looked pleased with himself and seemed to drift off into a reverie of his own until Groosh spoke again.

"Well?"

"Well what?"

"Can I go and see Rueggan?"

"If you must. But don't disturb him overmuch. If Graffyn finds out he'll try and charge us for the service — you know what he's like."

"Yes," Groosh agreed, before mumbling under his breath, "That's because someone not too far from here set him such a good example."

Groosh discovered Owhey sitting wedged between two rocks, watching the other dragonlets trying out their wings.

"I want you to come with me," said Groosh, his unseen approach making Owhey start. "It's about time we got you flying."

"No, Owhey is not trying to fly until the others gone," the little dragon protested, certain Groosh meant him to resume the training programme.

"Don't worry. We're going on a little trip to find out if someone else can help you."

"Who?"

"Wait and see. All I can say is he's very, very special. Now climb up on my back and we'll be off. Unless, of course, you'd sooner fly yourself?"

Owhey visibly brightened. If Groosh meant to fly then the dragon must be intending to cover some distance. For a dragonlet who had never left the area immediately surrounding Cairn Tor, this was a real adventure.

"Hold on tightly," Groosh warned, as soon as Owhey had scrambled up between his huge, curving wings. "I don't want to lose you if we run into some rough weather."

Groosh took two steps and was airborne, riding an updraft of warm air that bore them effortlessly, higher and higher until, having decided he had gained sufficient altitude, the dragon banked sideways and began to glide away from Cairn Tor as smoothly as a stick riding upon the back of a broad river.

As they travelled, Groosh shouted back a continual commentary above the windrush, drawing Owhey's attention to the finer points of aviation and the names of the places over which they flew.

Keldorran's unbroken green carpet, rolling away until it fused with the horizon. The Mountains of Kappah off to the east, their summits seeming level with Groosh's wingtips, reflecting sunlight from glaciers and snowfields. The Bowl of Munn, a shallow depression in Keldorran's otherwise uniform sprawl where, it is said, the Bahl-Witch commands a pack of evil, howling bonesnappers, bidding them to go forth beneath the cover of darkness to steal the young of all races as they sleep. Behind them, the black ragged peaks forming the Waste of Shugg, issuing a silent challenge to any who dare walk their bleak pathways and passes to return alive.

"Look Owhey, The Krystellate Obelisk!" Groosh called, some time later, nodding his head towards a finger of sculpted white rock rising defiantly from a small hill.

"We going there?" asked Owhey.

"No. Not today. Although, if you want, we'll fly in for a closer look."

"Yes, let me see! Let me see!" cried Owhey.

As they cleared the edge for Keldorran, Groosh warned Owhey to hold on tightly, and dived towards the ground, levelling out just above the tree tops. Owhey whooped with excitement. Groosh continued to accelerate, his shadow racing across the ground before them until the wind fairly howled about Owhey's ears. Soon, sky and ground melded into one continuous blur, and the little dragon felt his own, small voice crying out in exhilaration. It was as though he and Groosh had dissolved and become part of the sky itself. In less time than it took Owhey to blink, Groosh had cut up the hill, following the contours perfectly, and then shot skywards again, appearing above the Obelisk's tower where the huge Dom Krystal threw spears of energised light in all directions.

"Look at that bunch of mudheads," Groosh chuckled, looking down upon a knot of Apprentices, their noses in their books, "they haven't even noticed us. Why, I could singe the hats off the lot of them before they so much as twitched a whisker!"

"Go on!" Owhey urged.

"Better not," replied Groosh, smiling to himself, "Grunch would really give us both an ear-bashing for a stunt like that. Besides, we've got business to attend to."

It was Owhey's turn to smile. He quite liked the idea of being told off for doing something daring for a change.

When Groosh finally touched down outside Rueggan's cave in the Valley of Wendlock, Owhey was reluctant to climb down. He could quite happily have spent the day in the sky for he had started to pretend they were his wings, not Groosh's, that scythed through the air. Back on the ground he was painfully reminded of his limitations, especially now that he knew what it felt like to *really* fly.

Two Gorphs, who had been playing at the entrance of Rueggan's cave-workshop, sprang upright when Groosh landed with a whirring of wings, and scampered off, jabbering at the top of their voices.

Presently, a halo of smoke resting about his shoulders and a fine layer of ash upon his beard and eyebrows, Rueggan appeared; the two Gorphs now poking their heads from beneath the wizard's tunic.

"Hello. Groosh, isn't it?" he asked, trying to waft away the smoke from his eyes. "And who's the little firedrake?"

"Owhey," Groosh replied.

"Well, hello to Owhey as well," said the wizard, jovially, his eyes flashing quickly beneath the heavy eyebrows.

Owhey nodded politely. He had heard that wizards were not adverse to turning anyone who upset them into a croakhopper and he had no wish to put it to the test.

"So what brings you? A parcel? Some news? Want to adopt a Gorph, perhaps?"

The Gorphs chattered in annoyance at this last proposal and stared at their master with disapproval.

"We come to ask your advice," Groosh began. "I have heard that you have built a flying machine. Is this true?"

"A gliding machine," Rueggan replied. "As you know, the difference between flying and gliding is an important one. Though I wish I had, as you put it, built a flying machine, I am afraid I would not want to make such a claim myself." He looked at Groosh and then pointed to the dragon's wings. "Anyway, why would you want to know? A flying machine would be about as much use to you as a hole would a Trolle."

"You're not the only one to tell me that," replied Groosh, wryly. "No, I do not ask for myself but for young Owhey here. He's having a bit of trouble getting started and I thought you might have an idea of how we might get him launched."

"I have," said Rueggan. "Wait until he's ready." He regarded Owhey. "I can't improve on Nature, young fellow. It takes me all my time to copy it. Why don't you be patient?"

"You're right, of course," agreed Groosh, hurriedly, noticing Owhey on the verge of another tearful outburst, "but Owhey is really a bit behind schedule and it's starting to worry him terribly."

"So I see. Well, I think your timing is most fortunate for, whilst

I cannot help, I'm expecting several guests a little later and I shouldn't be at all surprised if one of them can help you out, if you'd care to wait."

"Thank you. If it will not cause inconvenience, Owhey and I would be most grateful, wouldn't we?"

Owhey nodded emphatically.

"On the contrary," Rueggan beamed, "I believe you might help me." He lifted his tunic and shoo-shooed the Gorphs out. "If Owhey plays with the Gorphs I'd like to take a few measurements of your wings for my research, if I may."

"My pleasure," Groosh agreed.

Rueggan bowed gracefully before turning to the Gorphs. "Right you two, take Owhey and play nicely. No, and I mean NO mischief. Understand?"

The Gorphs nodded, seized Owhey by the paws, and dragged him off to play, giggling and gurgling happily.

Turfen, Doyen of the Council of Wizards, arrived at the head of a column of shovel and axe wielding Trolles. He bade the Trolles wait quietly while he spoke to Rueggan. The Trolles nodded and sat down to play 'smack-knuckles' amongst themselves while he walked forward.

"Hail Doyen!" said Rueggan, giving Turfen the benefit of a broad smile at the same time as his official title. "What brings you from the Obelisk?"

"The need for fresh air," Turfen replied. "Someone had to accompany the Trolles down to the plains by the river to clear a new field for planting next Reawakening, so I thought I'd volunteer myself and pay my good friend a visit on the way through." He smiled, first at Rueggan, and then at Groosh. "Greetings, Groosh. What do you do today?"

Between them, Groosh and Rueggan explained Owhey's problem, ending with a request for Turfen's advice and, if possible, help.

"Sounds as though it's in the mind rather than the wings," Turfen observed, adopting a professional tone.

"I'm certain of it," Groosh agreed. "Can you do anything?"

"I do have an idea. I'm not sure if it'll work or not — my research in this particular field is incomplete, you see — but I'm willing to try."

"What are we waiting for," enthused Rueggan, who has always been fond of anything new. "I'll take you to him."

At Rueggan's call the two Gorphs returned, followed by Owhey. They were all covered, toe to tail, in a variety of coloured splotches, dots and lines.

"Oh, no," Rueggan groaned. "They've been in my dye pots again. It takes ages to get rid of and gets on everything."

"Like the Gorphs," laughed Turfen.

"Unfortunately, yes," Rueggan replied.

Seeing that something was afoot, something which might be more interesting than 'smack-knuckles', the Trolles gathered around the group, watching attentively. When Turfen produced a small krystal affixed to a long chain it became obvious that the wizard meant business, and the Trolles sat down, nudging and jostling to get a better view.

"Right, Owhey, I want you to do exactly as I tell you," Turfen began, reassuringly. "There is nothing to be scared of."

"You making me fly?" Owhey asked, hopefully.

"That's the general idea," replied Turfen. "Now I want you to watch this krystal closely and don't take your eyes off it. Just listen to my voice and think of nothing else, do you understand?"

Owhey nodded. So did the two Gorphs.

"Watch the krystal, follow its every movement, back and forth, back and forth . . ." Owhey complied as best he could but was distracted by the sight of the two Gorphs, sitting next to Turfen, watching the krystal intently.

"Your eyes are getting tired, you want to sleep, sleep, sleep, you want to close them and sleep, sleep . . ." Turfen's voice was a controlled, relaxing monotone. "Sleep, sleep, sleep . . ."

Owhey dutifully closed his eyes. So did the Trolles and the Gorphs.

"Stretch out your wings, stretch them out, feel how strong

they are . . ."

Owhey stretched his wings amid the sound of shovels and axes falling to the ground as the Trolles stretched out their arms. Turfen, his concentration centered solely upon the dragonlet, continued softly.

"They are strong wings. Wings that are strong enough to lift you into the air, strong enough to let you fly. Can you feel how strong they are?"

"Yes!" everyone chorused at once.

"When I tell you, you are going to flap your wings; you are going to fly, aren't you?"

"Yes!" everyone affirmed.

"One . . . two . . . three! Flap, Owhey! Flap! Fly, Owhey! Fly!"

An amazing scene ensued. As Owhey, quite unaffected by Turfen's influence, did as he was asked and flapped his wings vigourously, the whole company of Trolles, along with the two Gorphs, rose to their feet and began running in all directions at once, flapping their arms wildly. They ran into each other, bounced off tree trunks, flapped into Rueggan's workshop and cannoned off rocks. Owhey stayed put.

"Oh, dear! It doesn't appear to work on dragons," said Turfen, obviously disappointed.

"It works on Trolles, though," observed Rueggan, the sound of crashing and banging issuing from his workshop making him wince.

Groosh, even though he knew he should not, began to titter uncontrollably. When the Trolles and the two Gorphs all grouped together at once in the 'V' formation of Honkah-birds and ran off down the valley, still flapping, it became too much to bear and he collapsed in fits of laughter.

"Remarkable! Absolutely remarkable!" exclaimed Rueggan. "I've never seen anything like it!"

"Well, I'd better go and round them up," replied Turfen, the colour drained from his face. "This is embarrassing!"

"Not to worry," gasped Groosh, between breaths, "they're probably building nests!" He guffawed with such mirth he began to snort flames.

"No," said Rueggan flatly, "it's the wrong season." Then he too began to shake as a fit of laughter took hold of him.

It took some time before Groosh and Rueggan could collect themselves and turn their attention to Owhey. The dragonlet failed to see what there was to be so happy about. He still could not fly.

"Never mind," Rueggan comforted, wiping the tears from his eyes. "Come and help me to clean up in the cave. Shepf is due soon and he might have an idea."

"I can't wait; I really can't," sniggered Groosh to himself.

Shepf's arrival was felt before the wizard himself was seen. A gentle breeze, appearing from nowhere, suddenly sprang up, sighing through the branches of the surrounding trees, and playfully chasing flower petals across the ground before it. Moments later, clad in robes to match the colour of the sky, the wizard swept into view, his tunic billowing around him.

"Always a bit of a showoff," observed Rueggan, lightly, "but a thoroughly decent sort underneath it."

Shepf's solution to Owhey's plight was, not surprisingly, concerned with wind summoning.

After getting Owhey to face him with wings outstretched, the wizard called up winds of varying strength; beginning with a fresh breeze and ending with a full-blown gale which picked Owhey up, turned him upside down, and dumped him in the crown of a tree. Groosh was too concerned with Owhey's welfare to start laughing again, especially when the dragonlet began crying with fear and frustration. Thankfully, Rueggan was a practical individual first and a spell-caster second, and he soon brought out a long ladder in preference to Shepf's idea of blowing Owhey out again, effecting the young dragon's rescue himself.

Once safely back on the ground, there was no consoling Owhey. He sobbed until his cheeks were wet with tears, and continued until they stained the dry earth at his feet. No amount of reassurance from Groosh or the two magicians could stop him.

"Tears on such a wonderful day?" Graffyn walked over and knelt down by Owhey, stroking his mane. "Who's made you cry, little fellow? Tell Graffyn and he'll sort them out."

The wizards and Groosh all looked guilty.

"We've been trying to help him fly," Groosh offered, lamely.

"Is that all," replied Graffyn. "I can't see why that should cause tears." He continued petting Owhey.

"We've tried everything," said Rueggan, "and nothing worked."

"Ah, well," Graffyn said, close to Owhey's ear. "That's because they haven't got any of my super-special Flying Dust."

Owhey stopped crying and looked searchingly into Graffyn's face.

"Flying dust?" he asked, uncertainly.

"Why, yes. I've got a pouch full here," Graffyn produced a tightly woven bag closed witha drawstring.

"Stop teasing, Graffyn," scolded Shepf. "This is no time to go playing your tricks."

"Tricks! Me? Never!" Graffyn replied, looking hurt. "If you'll step over here I'll show you."

"There's no such thing as Flying Dust and well you know it," Rueggan said, sternly.

"Well, that's where you're wrong," retorted Graffyn. "This dust of mine," he said, holding the bag aloft, "never ever fails. It works, I tell you."

"You've been asleep in the sun for too long," said Shepf. "Now stop your nonsense and start behaving."

"Do you really want to fly?" Graffyn asked, looking directly at Owhey.

"Of course he does!" growled Shepf. "Now I've told you . . ."

"Owhey must answer for himself," interrupted Graffyn, cutting Shepf's protest off. "Now tell me, Owhey," he continued, "do you really want to fly?"

"Yes!" exclaimed Owhey.

"Are you sure?"

"Yes!"

"More than anything else?"

"Yes! Yes! Yes!"

Graffyn paused, as if making up his mind about something. "Alright, I believe you," he said, at length. So if I were to give you my bag of Flying Dust you wouldn't give it to anyone else?"

"No! Never, ever!" Owhey promised.

"Good! Than fly you shall," Graffyn proclaimed with certainty. "You are not to listen to anyone else, no matter what they tell you, and you must follow my instructions exactly or it won't work."

"I'll burn his beard off if he lets Owhey down," Groosh threatened, loud enough for everyone to hear.

Graffyn took no notice and continued his conversation with Owhey.

"Now, this is the most important part, and the most difficult. There is a secret rhyme which makes the Flying Dust work. If you forget it, then you might as well let me have my dust back. But if you can remember it, every last word, then I promise you, on my Spellbook, that in three days from now you'll fly for the first time."

"By my beard!" exclaimed Shepf. "He's sworn an oath on his Spellbook! If he fails he'll be banished from the Obelisk for life!"

Graffyn said nothing, he merely handed the bag to Owhey and said:

"This is the rhyme. We'll repeat it until I'm certain you know it by heart." He screwed up his face until his chin almost touched his nose. "Ah, yes, now I remember . . ."

GRAFFYN'S ACTIVATING RHYME

I must, I must, believe this dust,
Will make my wish come true,
I know my wings are wonderous things,
And will do what wings should do.

In this dust alone I trust,
And I promise not to cry,
For as sure as wizards all wear hats,
In three days I shall fly.

Graffyn made Owhey repeat the rhyme over and over until he was sure the dragonlet could say it without hesitation.

"Well, that's all there is to it," he concluded. "Starting tomorrow, as soon as you awake I want you to go somewhere, by yourself, say the rhyme and then throw a handful of dust over your wings. On the third morning, and only on the third morning, I want you to take a run, a jump, and fly. Simple, don't you think?"

"Graffyn is the greatest of all wizards I think," said Owhey, in open admiration.

Graffyn chuckled aloud. "Glad you think so. I tell you what, if it works . . . I mean, *when* it works, you might go and repeat what you've just said to Grunch."

"I will! I will!" Owhey promised.

Grunch listened to Groosh's report of the proceedings outside Rueggan's workshop in stony silence.

"I knew it! I knew it!" Grunch thundered, as soon as Groosh finished. "Wizards, if you can call Graffyn a wizard, have got no idea of anything beyond their spellbooks!"

"He did swear an oath," Groosh reminded. "Shepf assured me that he would never have done such a thing if he wasn't absolutely certain it would work."

"Typical! That Graffyn is more slippery than a bagful of Bobbols! He wouldn't know what an oath was if it bit him!"

"So what shall we do?"

Grunch looked as though he might explode. "Do?! There's nothing we can do, except wait!" He thumped a clenched paw against the cavern floor. "But I promise you, if we have to console Owhey, I'm going to burn every hair off his face!"

"You won't have to," said Groosh. "I've already told him what I'm going to do."

"Have you spoken to Owhey; tried to prepare him for the worst?" asked Grunch, suddenly concerned.

"I've tried," Groosh confessed, "but he won't listen. He's absolutely convinced Graffyn is the best thing since charcoal cookies."

"Then he's got a shock in store," said Grunch. "And so has that Graffyn!"

Owhey was a dragonlet transformed. He slept, deep and dreamless. He ate Flayla out of charcoal cookies. He played, he laughed, and he walked around Cairn Tor as though he were walking upon clouds. He neglected his wing-stretching exercises and occupied himself showing Tokkle pictures from a book. Only occasionally, when Flayla tried to discover the reason for his sudden euphoria, would Owhey grow quiet and reticent, and reply curtly: "In the dust alone I trust."

On the morning of the third day, Owhey sneaked from his family cave and walked up to the top of the nursery slope. It was a beautiful morning, bright and clear with hardly a breath of breeze to chase the dew mist from the lower slopes and hollows.

Almost reverently he repeated Graffyn's rhyme, threw the dust over his back and wings and then, with hardly a second thought, ran down the slope, his wings beating so fast they became a blur. Once, twice, he leapt and fell, but he kept on running until, just before the mattresses of sponge-plant, he launched himself into the air in a last, desperate attempt.

For a moment he appeared to hover uncertainly, hanging in the air with his paws clear of the rock. Then, as if someone has suddenly decided to wind in an invisible cord, Owhey executed an almost perfect vertical takeoff. He was flying!

"Grunch! Grunch! Come quick! You're not going to believe this!" Groosh burst into Grunch's cavern in a state of obvious excitement.

"I know, I know," retorted Grunch. "If you just wait here and listen, you'll find out what I mean. I was woken up at first light."

Hardly had Grunch finished than the sound of small wings, beating very quickly, filled the cavern, and Owhey's smiling face appeared suspended halfway between the floor and the ceiling.

"Grunchie, look! Graffyn is the greatest of all wizards!" he shouted. "Graffyn is the greatest of all!"

"Yes, yes, very nice. Now why don't you go and show Flayla what you can do."

"She's seen me! Everybody's seen me! I can fly! I can really fly!"

"Dear me," said Groosh, trying to hide a wide grin behind a paw, "it looks as though Graffyn's had the last laugh."

Grunch raised an eyebrow and regarded Groosh cooly.

"I'm not so sure," he replied. "This morning, just after Owhey told everyone about his wonderful Flying Dust, I took a peek at what was left in the bag Graffyn gave him."

"So?" Groosh said, completely baffled.

"It contained what I'm almost certain to be nothing but a herbal remedy of Wodema's for curing The Sneezes."

"So? . . ." Groosh pressed, still mystified. "I knew it wasn't really Flying Dust. There's no such thing."

Grunch smiled. "You know that, I know that, but there's a delegation of young Grumblypegs who've already left Cairn Tor to find Graffyn who think otherwise. Now I wonder what they're going to do when they discover they've walked from here to The Obelisk only to find out that Graffyn's Flying Dust . . ."

It's a smart wizard, a very smart wizard indeed, that manages to laugh at Grunch's expense.

THE THANE-KELD

Though undoubtably there are yet races unknown to us, The Obelisk Census continues to grow slowly as areas of Krystonia previously unexplored are charted and their inhabitants come forward to make themselves known, or are seen frequently enough for a detailed description to be made and corroborated by reputable witnesses. But there are those who remain a mystery even after sightings have been reported. Usually, these are unsubstantiated and rest upon the recollections of an individual who caught a fleeting glimpse in poor light conditions or, more commonly, 'thinks they saw something'. I am certain that the majority of reports of the latter type arrive as the result of an overactive imagination and fear of the dark. They rapidly become embellished in order to make their telling more entertaining, and as they pass from mouth to mouth and fireside to fireside, grow more exaggerated and colourful, and less factual. Soon they are almost total invention and become the means by which many a wandering storyteller obtains a warm fire and a hot meal on a stormy night. But whilst such stories come and go, a few have persisted through generations without suffering much alteration to their basic theme. There are those, myself included, who would swear an oath before the Doyen himself that they saw what they say they saw, and care not who believes them.

Occasionally, time has revealed the truth. The Hagga-beast which attacked a Maj-Dron caravan and was seen, and later described by a whole tribe of witnesses — the infant Shigger amongst them — finally put its existence beyond doubt and testified to the accuracy of many Maj-Dron folk songs which had been sung for generations. Other individual sightings occurring at different times and in different places have been so consistent that they appear to support each other and tip the balance away from doubt and towards belief.

In this way, several shadowy individuals have become part of our lore and legend. Each go by their own name and are surrounded by a wealth of strange and fascinating stories. Yet, until such times as their existence is proven beyond all doubt, all that is known of them remains apart from the main body of Krystonian knowledge and is set down in the dark scrolls of the Thane-Keld*.

*Translator's note:

No single word exists in our language which provides a direct translation of the Krystonian 'Thane-Keld'. The closest approximations I can make are 'Outsider' and 'Outcast'. Accurately translated, 'Thane-Keld' means 'One who waits beyond' in the same sense that we might refer to a person who refuses all invitations to join a group and stands apart, watching.

OKINOWAHTE

Everything about an Om-ba-Don speaks of strength. Its hands are so broad they might provide a comfortable seat for two Bobbols or even a medium sized Trolle. Its arms are powerful enough to hurl a giant snowball clear over the pinnacle of the Obelisk, or punch straight through the thick winter ice that forms on the waters surrounding their Tarnholds. On thickset legs it can carry prodigious loads up and down the treacherous glacier slopes of the Kappah the whole day through and never tire or once falter in its stride. It has been said — and I see no reason to disbelieve it — that if six Om-ba-Don were to challenge every wizard in the Krystellate Obelisk to a tug-o'-war, three would have to withdraw to make it a fair contest! Those of you who know of the terrible battle for possession of the Dom Krystal will recall how the clans of Om-ba-Don stood firm between The Obelisk and the massed ranks of N'Borg's heinous legions. Were it not for their timely appearance upon the battle ground, I would no longer be writing and Krystonians — those who were left — would be slaves enduring the everlasting winter of N'Borg's reign.

Awesome physical strength is matched by great inner fortitude. An Om-ba-Don prizes loyalty, honesty and courage above all other virtues, and a promise made is a promise never broken. Once an Om-ba-Don gives its word, every last syllable of their vow, it seems, might as well be etched upon their noble hearts forever. The Om-ba-Don Creed governs every moment of their lives and any would willingly embrace death sooner than break their bond and bring dishonour to their clan. This is the way of all Om-ba-Don: there are no exceptions.

By now you may be wondering what all this has to do with anything. How it is in any way connected to those who are Thane-Keld? Well, I believe it to be of the utmost importance when you ask yourself if the following tale be true, for it is largely concerned with the Om-ba-Don clans, the little-known snowfields of the high Kappah where only they tread, and with one Om-ba-Don in paticular.

Barloh was something of an oddity even by Om-ba-Don standards. He was born with feet of exceptional size. Whether it was this which set him apart right at the beginning of his life I cannot say, but from a very early age he went out of his way to avoid company with any but an infant Gowdan pack animal he called Kudd, preferring to wander alone in the high passes and little used tracks than work with the other members of his Sept on the mountain terraces. At first, his antisocial behaviour was frowned upon by the Elders. They felt it undermined the tightly knit comradeship the Om-ba-Don Creed and Code encouraged. But, as his knowledge of the mountains grew at a rate surpassed only by his feet, Barloh was invariably chosen whenever an urgent message or special delivery needed to be sent between the Tarnholds. Seemingly impervious to the weather conditions, he never lost his way and always arrived at his destination on time. To their credit, the Elders saw that this eccentric in their midst strengthened rather than weakened the clans and, whilst they thought it wise not to be seen condoning such aloofness, whenever he came to one of the Tarnholds they always ensured that Kudd was well-laden with provisions before he departed again. Their foresight was well. rewarded.

One particularly hard winter, when all the usual routes between the Tarnholds were blocked by heavy snow drifts which made communication hazardous, it was Barloh who found and signposted safe alternatives, and acted as guide for every important expedition the whole winter through. This silenced for good any remaining complaints and, when Barloh approached the Arch Elder to request permission to build his own cabin above the Line of Permanent Snows, he not only obtained consent, he was given the necessary materials and assistance to ensure a suitable dwelling was constructed to his liking in a very short space of time.

So Barloh the Pathfinder came to live and wander through

the mountain heights he loved, discovering short cuts, scouting out new areas suitable for crop terracing and sounding out his great Phargol-Horn in warning whenever an unexpected storm broke suddenly upon the peaks — often heard more than seen from one season to the next.

Though old, Barloh enjoys good health, and he and Kudd (whose sight is failing but knows the mountains so well he can still find his way unerringly), still persist in their solitary lifestyle. The only concession this big-footed Om-ba-Don has made to society at large is an infrequent visit to The Obelisk in order to validate the charts which show the passes — liable to change from one winter to the next — through which contact with the Maj-Dron is maintained.

It was during one such visit that I was fortunate enough to sit in his temporary encampment (for he steadfastly refused to sleep indoors even if they could find a space big enough to accommodate him) and heard him speak of the Snow Giant, Okinowahte.

Most Om-ba-Don will talk of Okinowahte, claiming to have heard his half-growl, half-howl when travelling at night. Some say they have felt the ground beneath them quake and tremble as he passed close by. A few believe they have caught sight of him, looming above them, his eyes blazing like torches, but admit to a certain amount of doubt. A blizzard can deceive the eyes and ears of the most experienced traveller and, perhaps, what they had seen had been nothing more than a pattern in the flying snowflakes, or a large rock outcrop whose outline had been momentarily obscured.

Other evidence is quite commonplace and takes various forms. Gigantic footprints — even bigger than four of Barloh's put together — sudden avalanches and rockfalls, or the overnight disappearance of a whole terrace of crops, are all taken as signs that Okinowahte is close. But there is nobody who has ever claimed, definitely, to have seen him.

Except Barloh the Pathfinder.

"Okinowahte walks when the wind comes from the North

carrying snow," Barloh began, lying on his back and looking at me through the gap between his huge feet. "He only likes to move when the air is full of snow, for in a blizzard Okinowahte is invisible. Who looks upward when they cannot even see their hand in front of their face? You might walk over one of his feet and think they were snowdrifts." He looked up at the stars. "They don't seem to shine as brightly down here as they do up in the Kappah," he observed, and then looked wistfully away towards the mountains, gilded by moonlight. "There is no other place that I would be on such a night as this."

"So you claim to have seen Okinowahte?" I pursued, fearing he might drift off the subject.

"Claim?" He gave me a withering look. "I have seen."

"When? How? What does he look like?"

Barloh regarded me with the resigned air of one who has told the same story too many times and cannot decide if he should tell it over again.

"Long ago," he finally replied. "Winter. When the snow fell for days without end and I only set foot outside to make sure Kudd had enough food in his manger."

Upon hearing his name mentioned, the Gowdan looked up and make a low, questioning rumble in its throat.

"No, Kudd. Not yet." Barloh smiled and shook his head. "He wants to be back in the mountains as much as I do."

"So you stayed in the cabin?" I prompted.

"No choice. It is only a fool who goes out in such weather. I made a good fire, boiled up plenty of broth, and made a new harness for Kudd's panniers."

Kudd looked up again, but this time Barloh ignored him and continued with his tale without me having to talk him back into it.

"I had been sleeping when, I know not why, I woke suddenly. When you live a long time alone you sense someone approaching before you see them."

I nodded in agreement. I knew exactly what he meant.

"I knew someone was outside: I could almost smell them. But

I kept telling myself not to think such thoughts. Nobody would venture out on such a night. So I poured out some broth and sat down to eat."

Barloh closed his eyes. I fancied his mind was showing pictures of that night on the inside of his eyelids and, in the brief pause before he resumed, I felt my beard begin to bristle involuntarily.

"Then came a noise: a sudden thump on my roof that shook the cabin to the timbers, followed by a scraping, scratching sound, as though something were trying to get in . . ."

(I had suddenly began to wish Barloh would invite me to sit a little closer to him!)

"I picked up my Clayda-axe and waited. Nothing. Only the sound of the wind, and I began to wonder if a rock had rolled down, landed on the cabin roof and slid off. I had just made up my mind that this must be the only sensible explaination when I heard Kudd begin making a terrific din. It was a sound I had never heard him make before."

Barloh screwed up his face as though hearing the sound again and trying to shut it out. "I grabbed my Clayda and ran out. The door on Kudd's stable was thrown open and, when I looked in, I saw he had gone. Thinking he had bolted, I looked for his tracks, but there were none. It was as if the blizzard had swallowed him without leaving a trace for me to follow. "I ran back to the cabin, put on my heaviest cape and went out, calling for him at the top of my voice, shouting into the wind, and had not gone far when I thought I heard him.

'Unsure if it were my imagination, I ran forward and, to my surprise and relief, found him standing at the bottom of a sheer-sided pit that had been dug out of the snow, still bawling his head off. Looking back, it seems strange I never stopped to wonder how the pit had got there and how Kudd had come to be in it: he's much too used to the mountains to have fallen in accidentally. Anyway, I had to dig him out which, I can tell you, would have been no simple task on a clear day. And all the time I worked, I felt as if my every move were being watched."

"By Okinowahte?"

Barloh shrugged. "It is possible."

"Then what?"

"Then I returned to my cabin to find that three timbers had been torn from the roof. When I went inside my bed was covered with snow and my broth had vanished from the fire, cooking bag and all."

"Okinowahte had taken your broth?"

"Again, it is possible," Barloh replied, noncommitally.

"Why do you doubt it?" I asked. "It seems obvious."

"The wind only speaks of what it has seen: the snow only of where it has lain. Such is the way of the Om-ba-Don. Too many words make a liar," Barloh replied, sagaciously.

I agreed, and asked him to continue, but could not help thinking how, for a race who claim to mistrust words, the Om-ba-Don have a fondness for profound statements.

"For the next two days, nothing further occurred. I repaired the roof as best I could, ensured my fire burned brightly, and took the precaution of securing Kudd's stable with a heavy beam across the door. He seemed a little insulted, but I was acting in his best interests. Then, late into the second night he began calling out once more in alarm.

'This time, when I got outside, both Kudd and his stable had gone."

"Did I hear your correctly? The stable had gone?"

"Vanished," Barloh confirmed. "Save for two of the supporting posts, Kudd and his stable might have been swallowed by the mountains."

"Taken by Okinowahte?"

"The wind speaks only . . ."

"Yes, I know. Please, continue."

"Again I set out to find him. But I made a mistake that might have ended in the Sleep without a Morning. Instead of testing my step upon the fresh snow, I ran, like a fool from the lowlands, and didn't see the crevasse until it was too late. The snow beneath me collapsed, swept me off my feet, and carried me over the edge. I recollect falling and thinking the Kappah had finally taken Barloh as their own. A long way I fell, in a shower of snow. Then I hit something hard — a rock or an ice ledge I suppose — which jarred me from my senses.

'Yet, as you see, Barloh sits before you and did not perish. Had I have lain out in such weather overnight, I should have surely slept for all time. But I was saved. I was lifted from the crevasse."

"By Okinowahte?"

This time Barloh did not correct me. He nodded in agreement.

"Yes. I felt myself lifted upwards but, still feeling the effects of my fall, saw only the stars and the mountain peaks when I opened my eyes. I wondered, as I rose back up the crevasse, if I would never stop, and float up and up until I lay amongst the stars themselves. Then I saw him and understood."

Barloh shook his head as though it were still difficult to believe.

"Okinowahte was holding me in his hand! Me, Kephren! Just look! Compare my size to yours! And yet I was held as though I were . . . a Bobbol. No, less even!"

For once, I was too shocked to think of anything to say.

"You cannot begin to imagine his size. No Tarnhold could stand against him. No crevasse could have concealed him."

"Did he speak?" I asked; it being the first question to suggest itself.

"No. I lay looking up into his face. He stood looking down at me, his head far away, somewhere in the sky. Then he bent down, his face coming closer. All fur, white fur all over, and a mouth, I think, big enough to swallow me easily. And eyes. They are what I remember most. The eyes of Okinowahte. They burn like torches, yellow torches!"

Barloh became quiet.

"Then? What next, Barloh?"

"My head filled with darkness. I remember nothing else. Others know better than I what occurred. My next sight was of the walls inside a Tarnhold dormitory.

"Yes. I think Moplos once mentioned it. Wasn't it he that found you?"

"It was he who was first to answer the door," Barloh answered. "The clan were all abed when, so I am told, the Tarnhold was shaken to the foundations. At first, they thought it was a tremor — occasionally the mountains of the high Kappah can growl as they do at Cairn Tor —but when a second shock occurred they leapt from their beds, snatching up their axes. Moplos was first to the main door, and was about to open it when its heavy timbers were split assunder, and he was thrown backwards. Now certain the clan were under attack, he charged out, wielding his axe, only to find me lying in the snow, with Kudd *and* his stable close by.

"Did Moplos see Okinowahte?"

"No. Not a single member of the clan saw anything. They put me to bed, stabled Kudd, and mounted a guard through what remained of the night. They were at a loss to explain my appearance until I regained my senses and related my story."

"They believed you?"

"Some thought I had Snow-Madness, but when it was obvious I was fully recovered they accepted my word without question. It is not in the Om-ba-Don nature to knowingly tell an untruth."

"So you were saved by Okinowahte. Incredible!"

Barloh, satisfied his tale was told, got to his feet and covered the fire with a clod of earth.

"Have you ever seen him since that time?" I asked, not wanting to waste this rare opportunity to hear of an encounter first hand.

"No. But when the snow falls from the breath of the north wind for days without ceasing, I cook a whole bag of the Om-ba-Don broth and leave it outside my cabin. It is always gone come the morning."

"Have you not tried to see him? To talk? Perhaps he would join the Great Design and rid us of N'Borg's foul name?"

"You're not the first to suggest such a thing," replied Barloh. "You must understand, Okinowahte belongs to a greater design.

He is part of the snow and the wind, of the mountains themselves. He was born when the mountains were born: he will endure as they endure. It is enough for me to know he watches and will come if he ever thinks I need him."

"I thought the wind spoke only of what it had seen," I reminded.

"So it does," agreed Barloh. "And when you have lived long enough in the mountains, Kephren, you learn to listen to what it is saying. Do not make the mistake of thinking that only wizards know magic. There are many different types of magic in these lands. More than you know . . ."

GULBAR-GUL

Marle is one of the smaller coastal settlements, with a resident population rarely exceeding fifty adults. It is quiet, picturesque, and can only be reached by a narrow path, hardly wide enough to let two travellers pass, which threads its way down the face of the vertical cliffs of red stone looming above the houses. It is a path seldom used by any save for Marle's own fish-watchers, and the occasional artist or poet who come claiming to draw inspiration from the scenery, but who really simply appreciate the timelessness and tranquility of the place.

When the days are long and hot, and the sea is calm and clear, two or three of the settlement dwellers ascend the cliffs and, from their high vantage point, watch the sea for the huge shoals of flipskipper fish which abound in the area. Once a good shoal is located, they signal to their brethern far below by clapping long, flat timber boards together. By the number and tone of the claps, the other men of Marle know exactly where the fish are and take to their strange oval-shaped vessels to net them. On their return, the wives clean the catch, hang it out on a spiked frame to dry in the sun and then place them in small, conical smoke-ovens; throwing herbs upon the damp wood-shavings to give the fish its unique and distinctive flavour. Marle flipskipper is famous and, due to both its taste and properties of preservation, commands a high trade value when the Gadazorri sailors drop anchor close to the shore.

But Marle has become renowned for more than a local delicacy. Strange, thick fog often rises unexpectedly from the sea after nightfall; and with the fog comes Gulbar-Gul.

Ask any resident of Marle if they have seen Gulbar-Gul and they will reply, "Of course! Who hasn't?" But ask them what he looks like and they are less certain, giving a vague description of something dark, long of neck, that moves slowly over the land with a shuffling, awkward gait. It is impossible to see this night visitor clearly, for he keeps hidden in the thickest part of the fog as though he were scared of being recognised. He smells strongly of rotting seaweed and cries out incessantly: a long, mournful, wailing cry that has resulted in many of the locals wearing plugs of cloth in their ears when they retire to bed on a foggy night. Yet, apart from this minor inconvenience, Gulbar-Gul causes no distress or damage. Quite the opposite. He retreats quickly at the sound of approaching footsteps or raised voices.

So why does he choose to leave the santuary of the sea to creep and crawl amongst the houses? What is it that draws him to Marle season after season and to neglect more isolated parts of the coastline? To explain I must speak of a time when Marle was even smaller and more isolated than now.

In winter, when the wind whips the sea into high waves, Marle lies protected by a finger of rock that projects from the base of the cliffs and runs diagonally from the shore out into the sea. The Throne of Birds, as the rock is called, still shields most of the settlement houses to this day but, once, less than a dozen houses huddled behind its red flanks. They were all built so that their doors and windows faced each other in order that their occupants had no need to leave the warmth and security of their own homes to converse with their neighbours. The weather, the size of the catch and the repair of vessels were the main topics of conversation. Anything beyond this was news indeed; be it the sighting of a passing stranger on the cliff tops or some interesting piece of flotsam thrown up on the shore. Nothing aroused greater interest than the birth of a new member of the community, and the subsequent naming and raising of the infant became a matter for intense discussion and argument. So imagine the excitement when, one Reawakening, it was discovered that Marle was expecting not one but three new arrivals at the same time!

At the end of the Season of Harvest, two males and one female child were born within two days of each other and, it was generally agreed, never had Marle seen such well-featured, strong and blithe-natured infants. This seemed to confirm the opinion that great magic had been involved and that, in the course of their lives unfolding, the names of Odan, Drago and Nemone would endure long after their bodies were given back to the sea.

And so it transpired.

By the end of their fourteenth Season Cycle, Odan and Drago were already taller than most of the other men of Marle. Their skin, tanned by the sea, wind and sun, was bronzed and without blemish. Their gaze was steady, their bearing confident and their frames lithe and muscular. Both were inseparable, even going as far as to build a slightly larger vessel than usual in order to fish side by side. But handsome though Odan and Drago undoubtedly were, Nemone made them seem ordinary.

Her eyes were the same fathomless, emerald hue of the sea on a calm day. Her skin possessed the delicate translucence of a ghost-shell and her hair tumbled about her shoulders in waves of spun silk that seemed to capture and hold light. Everything about her, in looks, manner and movement, appeared to shine. To the boys, returning from the sea with their catch of fish, she seemed to radiate like a star amongst the drab aproned women waiting on the shore. Before long, both were hopelessly in love with her.

Soon the two boys were competing openly for her affections. If Odan found her a pretty shell, Drago would scour the shore until he found two. If Drago dived off a high cliff ledge into the sea, Odan would risk his life to dive off one higher. They no longer fished from the same boat, each believing that even this was an opportunity to impress Nemone by bringing home a larger catch than their rival. For now rivalry had extinguished friendship.

Nemone could see what was happening and it lay heavily upon her heart. She loved both equally and hated to stand by and watch their jealousy consume them and spur them to ever greater extremes. She tried refusing to speak to them, but this inflamed the situation yet more. Each accused the other of deliberately causing her rejection. In desperation she took advice.

One of the older women, who acted as healer for the settlement, was renowned for her wisdom. It was to her that Nemone went to speak of her dilemma and ask for a solution.

The woman thought long before replying: "If you cannot choose, then you must either leave Marle forever, take your own life, or agree to let the sea choose for you."

Nemone was, understandably, not in favour of either of the first two options.

"How will the sea choose?" she asked.

"Tell the boys they must row out into the sea and cast their nets once and once only. He who returns with the most fish will be your betrothed. Simple."

Simple the solution may have been, but Nemone could not bring herself to accept the old woman's counsel. She continued, trying to reconcile her two suitors until their behaviour left her in no doubt that she must resolve the situation once and for all.

One day, upon their return home, both boys had approached her. She had smiled at both in turn. They proffered small gifts. She accepted with equal grace. Both then asked if she would accompany him for a walk along the cliff tops. She said she would be happy for both to escort her. And off they had gone, Odan taking one arm, Drago linking the other. All went peacefully until Drago tried to pull her a little closer. Odan, sensing this, responded likewise. Soon, the situation escalated into a tussle which nearly wrenched poor Nemone's arms from their sockets!

"Enough! Enough!" she cried. "I cannot bear this any longer!"

"Yes, choose Nemone," urged Odan. "You must!"

"I will! I will!" she conceded, close to tears. "But if I do you must both give me your promise to abide by my decision."

They readily assented.

"And that you will be friends once more."

The boys were not so decisive about this.

*inowahte, the Bahl-witch, Gulbar-gul and Zarak are names which are only written in the
rk scrolls of the Thane-Keld.*

"You must promise me or I shall not choose."

They promised, half-heartedly.

"I vow that should I ever discover that one of you has spoken or acted ill towards the other I shall take my life, my own life, as forfeit. Do you agree?"

Both were a little surprised but, blinded by their desire to win her hand, both accepted the conditions on their oath.

When Nemone told the boys of the solution forwarded by the old woman they were quick to accept. Given their livelihood, it seemed fitting their fate should be decided by the sea and agreed, that come the dawn, they would both go forth and receive the sea's verdict.

"You must know," Nemone said softly, before they took to their vessels, "I love you both equally and always shall. It is you who have chosen this. I shall love the victor no more or no less than I shall love the loser, no matter which the sea chooses."

"And I shall love you," replied Odan.

"As shall I," echoed Drago.

"And you both remember the promise made upon my life?"

The boys nodded solemnly then, spontaneously, embraced briefly and wished each other luck.

Nemone smiled. Perhaps they really would be friends again.

Odan was first to cast his net and, to his great relief and Drago's equal horror, pulled it into his boat heavy with fish. Drago threw his and, from the shore where every member of the settlement had now gathered, was seen to drag in a net of fish to equal Odan's.

They returned and stood apart whilst the fish were counted —twice, to make absolutely sure of the correct result. When it was announced, Odan threw up his arms in delight. Drago slumped, distraught, to his knees and buried his face in the sand. He cursed the sea. He had lost Nemone, the star of his life, for want of two tiny fish!

Nemone was both relieved and sorrowful. She felt Drago's hurt as though it had been her own.

"Drago! Oh, Drago! You must remember your promise. My

life depends upon it!"

"I shall not break it," he replied, the words bitter as poison in his throat. "You are Odan's. The sea has chosen."

Nemone stroked his hair lightly. "See Odan," she said, motioning for her betrothed to draw close. "This I give to Drago as a token of my love for him." She took off a small, delicate necklace of shells and placed it about Drago's neck. Odan's eyes flashed with scarcely concealed jealousy.

"You love him more than me?" he demanded.

"No. The same. This you knew."

Odan swallowed his anger. "Yes. This I knew."

"But the sea has chosen," said Nemone. "I am your betrothed and shall keep myself only unto you for all my days."

There was nothing more to say.

Aware of their promise, and the terrible forfeit should either of them break it, Odan and Drago ceased their open conflict and made some show of civility whenever Nemone saw them together. But friendship's seed finds no fertile soil in words, only in heartfelt sentiment, and they simply avoided one another — not an easy task in such a small, closely knit community. Both still carried a black worm in their hearts; one which gnawed and gnawed at the fibre of their beings and denied them peace. For Drago, the sight of Nemone was sufficient to make him boil with hatred and jealousy for Odan. And, for Odan, every smile Nemone gave to Drago, every time he saw her necklace about his neck, sent darts to prick his skin. He longed to tear it from Drago's neck, remove all the traces and reminders of the love he knew she still bore within. He did not have long to wait before a suitable opportunity presented itself.

The small craft used by the fishermen of Marle are light and manoeuverable; ideal for skimming easily across the surface of a becalmed sea, but unsuitable for heavy weather. This presents few problems. It is rare indeed that a storm springs up so suddenly it catches the men unawares and, should their boat overturn, the people of Marle are almost as comfortable in the water as they are on land, and can swim back to the shore before the storm reaches its height.

On this occasion, the boats had moved further from the shore than was customary, harrying the shoals of flipskipper, when the wind changed direction without warning. Rapidly it gained strength, chivvying the sea until it began to show flecks of white foam along the wave crests.

The fishermen responded quickly, rowing hard for the shore. All, that is, except for Odan and Drago. Each saw it as an unspoken challenge; a way to test the other's nerve. So there they sat, waiting, as the waves grew beneath them, pitching and tossing the small vessels as though they were nothing more than spent leaves.

Now the wind, blowing away from the shore, caught them and began to push them out to sea. Odan was first to break, alarmed by the increasing amount of water sloshing about his ankles in the bottom of the boat. Drago, satisfied he had proved himself to be the braver, began to follow, amazed by the way he rose and fell on the back of the groundswell: one moment flying level with the top of the cliffs it seemed; the next plunged into the bottom of a valley whose flanks were formed by dark, seething water.

Odan, feeling his boat begin to wallow and grow heavy as it struggled to carry its water burden, chanced to look back over his shoulder. He saw Drago, high on a wave, suddenly capsize and vanish into the roaring face. He turned and began to row towards the point where Drago had disappeared, the wind against his back pushing him on.

There was a flash of skin, pale and diffused in the dark water. Then, in the trough between two waves, Drago's head appeared.

Their eyes met. Drago's were wide with fear; his mouth open sucking in precious air. Momentarily, Odan saw not his rival for Nemone's affections, but the face of his childhood ally. He dug his oar deep, driving the small boat towards his drowning friend.

A wave came. Drago vanished. Odan turned his boat into the wave, rode up its flank, breasted the top, and slid down into a trough once more. Drago's head broke the surface, now within arms' length. Odan stretched out. Drago clawed frantically. Then Odan saw the necklace and his visage clouded.

In one swift movement he tore it free. Drago's eyes widened with disbelief.

"No! Odan!" he screamed.

Odan raised the heavy wooden oar above his head and struck downward, hard.

Odan had reached exhaustion point when he felt the sand between his feet and knew he was safe. He had been some distance from the shore when the boat succumbed to the sea and left him with no choice than to dive into the thundering water and battle against the fierce undertow. As he staggered into the arms of the waiting men he suddenly remembered what he was holding. Unseen, he tucked it into the pouch sewn on the side of his breeches.

"Is Drago . . ."

"Lost," confirmed Odan, still gasping for breath. "I tried to . . ."

"We saw you turn back. You did what you could. The sea may give and the sea may take away," the fishermen comforted.

Odan was strong and, physically, was soon recovered. His conscience was a different matter. Though he would have previously welcomed Nemone crying upon his shoulder, now her grief fed his guilt. Worst of all were Nemone's observations that she would take comfort in the knowledge the boys had parted as friends and that Odan would always have her respect for having risked his own life for the sake of another. Drago's memory haunted him. Odan slept little and ate less. Only the thought that Nemone belonged to him alone, body and soul, eased the disgust he had begun to feel for himself.

Some five or six seasons later, there came a day when all the men of the settlement left to climb the cliff path and search inland for new timber. They would be gone for three or four days and, though he hated the thought of being parted from his

Nemone for a moment more than he had to, Odan knew he was expected to go with the others as part of his duty to Marle. He held Nemone to him, smelling the perfume of her skin and feeling the wonderful gossamer tresses of her hair between his fingers. Unable to contain himself, he kissed her for the first time. She responded. Each swore their love for the other. When Odan returned they would swear their final vows of betrothal.

For the first time since Drago's death, Odan felt truly happy, and he set off up the steep path singing, waving down to Nemone until he vanished from sight over the top of the cliff. While he was away, Odan would collect enough timber to weather-dry for a new house. A new home for himself and Nemone.

Likewise, Nemone's thoughts turned to their future. She had noticed how worn Odan's breeches were about the knees. She would make him a new pair to celebrate his return and the consumation of their betrothal. He would like that.

Timber is not the only raw material difficult to find in Marle. So is fibre, though, nowadays, trade with the Gadazorri ensures a good supply of quality cloth for sewing garments. But Nemone lived at a time when any contact with other races was rare and, in order to make Odan a new pair of breeches, she not only needed the small quantity she possessed for repairs to her own clothing, she required a substantial amount besides. As was the custom of the time, she made her intentions known to Odan's mother, who graciously donated a pair of her son's old breeches. Once the stitching was unpicked there should be more than enough for Nemone's requirements.

Nemone was as blissfully happy as any maid about to be betrothed. She sharpened her bone needles, selected several lengths of finest gut and began to unpick the stitched seams of Odan's old breeches. Then she noticed that there was still something contained in the pouch. She laughed. It was probably shells. Odan was always fond of pretty shells. Yes, look, a whole string of small ghost-shells . . .

When Odan reached the top of the cliffs and looked down upon Marle, nestled below, his heart sang with joy. He had cut timber enough to build his house. He would leave it to over-winter and return inland to collect it once it had been sufficiently weathered. By the end of the next season of Growth he would stand before his own hearth. He could not wait to share the news with Nemone and ran down the path faster than was sensible. But then, love is rarely sensible.

When Odan saw the women of Marle running out towards him he looked for Nemone. She was not with them. A bridal custom he did not know of, perhaps, he thought. But as soon as they were close enough for him to see their faces clearly, he knew something was amiss.

"Nemone? Where is Nemone?" he demanded.

"Oh, Odan," his mother cried, pulling him to her. "Odan, my son, she is gone."

"What nonsense is this!" he exclaimed, angrily.

"It is true, Odan, Nemone has gone, taken by the sea."

"What! When? How?" Odan felt suddenly sick in the pit of his stomach.

"The night you left. She went out upon the Throne of Birds and did not return."

"No! No! Nooo!"

When Odan walked into Nemone's little room he picked up her pillow and pressed it to his face, the faint smell of her perfume that lingered there both soothed and tortured him. He looked about. On a small table next to her bed a sprig of wild flowers she had picked on their last walk along the cliff tops. On the floor, carefully spread out, a few pieces of material, two bone needles and some gut. In the centre of the largest piece, a small necklace of ghost-shells lay, accusingly.

Odan was beyond comfort. He ran between the houses calling out "Nemone! Nemone!!" over and over. He would not speak to anyone. If they stood before him it was as though he looked through them, to somewhere far beyond.

For two days and nights he walked about the settlement

calling his lover's name. When, on the third morning, he was nowhere to be seen, Marle knew that the last of the three children had gone back to the sea.

That same night, the fog came in from the sea. And so did Gulbar-Gul.

Marle is little changed since the days of Drago, Odan and Nemone. More houses have been built and visitors, though still infrequent, are not as rare as they once were. Many have been woken in the night by the sound of Gulbar-Gul, calling mournfully as he wanders about the settlement, hidden in his shroud of fog. Some have suggested driving him away, but the residents of Marle will not permit such a thing. "After all," they say mysteriously, "one day you might lose your love."

ZARAK

Beneath the heat of the sun the glaciers and snowfields of the Kappah melt, drip by drip. Slowly, over time that makes my own life seem nothing but the blinking of an eye, the downward passage of the meltwater has scarred the face of the mountains with a web of interconnected channels. At the base of the great glaciers these are small and shallow, scarcely more than scratches, but as they descend the mountain sides they grow, increasing in width and depth, feeding the throats of deep ravines which roar and rage with torrents of foam-flecked water when the sun of Reawakening burns off the ice-burden of Winter. Many of these ravines have been skillfully dammed by the Om-ba-Don to create lakes about their clan Tarnholds; but many more plunge unchecked, down into the foothills and beyond to the gentler slopes of the lowlands, merging into clear-water streams that are the tributaries of the broad and winding River Cauld.

One of the largest streams that runs fast and deep, twisting its way through the foothills like a silver-backed serpent, has so eroded the rock underlying the shallow topsoil of the region that it turns and tumbles over its bed of broken stone constricted by sheer cliffs on either side. Many pathways trace the stream's course high above the surface of its white water but, without the aid of wings, it is impossible to actually drink from the stream itself as it rushes on far below. Thus Etheral — for so the stream is named — has long been a thorn in the sandal of travellers and traders. Providing one has a voice loud enough to overcome the roar of the water, it is quite possible for journeymen on opposite sides to hold a conversation or even to exchange parcels by throwing them across. Yet, though they may be close enough to discern the colour of each other's eyes, they cannot touch without undertaking a journey lasting anywhere up to two days for, along Etheral's entire length, only three places exist where it is possible to cross. Two of these are arching wooden bridges —tributes to the ingenuity of the great architect, Agoras, and the industry of his Trolle builders — which hang suspended between the rock walls of the gorge. If the crosswinds are not too strong, negotiating these presents few problems to the travellers providing they can bear the thought of only wooden planking separating them from death in the maelstrom below. But the third crossing; that is a different matter . . .

There is a point, just where the barren slopes of Kappah merge into wooded foothills, that Etheral encounters a rock fault and cascades down the vertical face, reforming in a boiling plunge-pool over which a rainbow curves. From the lip of the waterfall the cauldron which receives the broken body of the stream cannot be seen for the air is charged with water-mist, but by picking your way down to the waterfall's base, one may pass into another enchanted world.

Tiny flowers, that grow nowhere else in Krystonia, festoon the wet rocks, encrusting them with carpets of scarlet, yellow, orange and green. Mats of woven mosses hang, heavy and luxuriant, draping the outcrops on either side of the cascade with long, water-glistening tresses of purple and blue. The beauty of the place, so suddenly encountered, strikes dumb the unsuspecting traveller. This is as well: the thunder of the waterfall so fills the narrow gorge that all other sound is lost.

Where the bowl-shaped pool runs off and Etheral continues on its way to the River Cauld, a line of stones, fingers of black rock, thrust up from the stream bed and tear through the surface. The tips of these fingers are flat-topped and span the stream; the distance between each presenting a line of stepping stones spaced closely enough to tempt one to try and cross but far enough apart to make it a hair-raising experience. They are no ordinary stepping stones: this no ordinary place. These are the Singing Stones of Etheral and the narrow gorge the home of Zarak the Sorceress.

The slightest footfall upon the first stone begins the enchantment. It seems then the water takes on a voice, bidding the traveller cool their feet in the invigorating stream. Those who listen travel no more by land. The stone fingers begin to sink as though the hand from which they grew were slowly being clenched. In moments, the stones vanish below the surface, leaving the luckless traveller to be seized by the strong current.

It is said these victims are destined for more than a watery death, however. All knowledge contained in their minds, from birth to death, is taken from them by strange, eyeless, serpentile fish which congregate in the waters below the falls. Only then is the body released and given to the strong current of Etheral. These fish, spawned from the hair of Zarak, remember the debt they owe to the sorceress for their creation, and whisper all they have learned into her ear alone. Thus, little occurs in the interconnected watercourses of Krystonia, from the Kappah to the sea, which does not eventually reach Zarak.

It has not always been so, according to legend.

Once Zarak was but a beast of the narrow gorge. Then she ran, fleet of foot, upon four cloven hooves, feeding upon the flowers, nibbling the rafts of weed and blankets of moss which grow below the falls. She was as ignorant of magic as any beast, and seemed content to run and bound from rock to rock, ledge to ledge, rejoicing only in the strength of her legs. No cliff was too sheer, no ledge too narrow for Zarak. She wanted for nothing. Until one day, she stopped to listen to the Singing Stones . . .

Many a spellcaster in the Obelisk believes that somewhere beneath the surface of the pool lies a krystal to rival the Dom itself. Whether it be the water or some property inherent in the stone itself, unusual effects are produced: including the behaviour of the Singing Stones.

So Zarak came to stand upon the middle stone, bewitched by the music of the pool's waters. The stones began to sink, the water to pull at her legs, trying to sweep her into the swirling current. But Zarak was no weary traveller. In a single, powerful bound she leapt clear, landed safe upon the bank and ran as sure-footed as ever up the vertical side of the gorge.

It seemed she had escaped, but later, as she slept, strange voices filled her mind that spoke in tongues hitherto unknown. What they told only Zarak can say, but when the light of the early morning woke her it found her changed.

Where once she had been clothed entirely in coarse, brown hair, only her hinquarters remained unchanged. From the waist upwards she beheld naked skin. Her forlegs were arms, ending in hands with separate, nailed fingers. No longer could she move on all fours, instead she walked upright. The face which looked back at her from the mirror of a dew pool she knew not. It was not that of a beast but of a maiden. To a journeyman, the face would have seemed beautiful: to Zarak it was a hideous transformation.

Over the next few days further, more subtle changes occurred. Her mind, so long concerned only with finding food and shelter, now became preoccupied and restless, full of questions and thoughts that troubled her even in sleep. She yearned to speak of what had befallen her, yet could not bear the thought of anyone seeing her nakedness. She wanted to run, and keep on running, but could only totter uncertainly upon her hind legs. She thirsted for knowledge, yet cried bitterly for her former state of blissful innocence and ignorance. It seemed that two souls wrestled constantly within her and would not let her find peace.

Over time, Zarak has learned many words of power with which to shape her magic and serve her desires. She can calm the waters of Etheral or make them grow angry at a whim. She can halt the motion of the waterfall as though it were stone, not water, and cross from bank to bank without getting her feet so much as damp. Every hair she shakes from her mane becomes a servant serpent-fish awaiting her command. Some say she has discovered magic powerful enough to overcome death. Yet all her great powers cannot give her that which she desires most: the return of her beautiful cloven hooves.

So Zarak hides behind the waterfall of Etheral, too ashamed

of her appearance to let any see her, or ask for help. Instead she waits, certain that one day a traveller will stand upon the stones whose mind contains the words to reverse the enchantment. Unfortunately, neither she or the serpent-fish know that many travellers now take the precaution of carrying a small bag containing a pair of wooden earplugs.

Zarak may be waiting a long, long time.

THE BAHL WITCH

On stormy nights, when the wind rattled through the branches of the tree outside the house, my father would steal into my room as quietly as a ghost, perch on the end of my bed and, in his rich, resonant voice, spin yarns of fantastic beasts and faraway places that would fill my mind with wonderful pictures. Some were of his own invention, but most were tales which his own father had told him on similar occasions.

Most Krystonian adults can be relied upon to tell a good 'cradle story' or two as a means of entertaining and instructing their offspring and, nowadays, there is a greater exchange of stories between races than ever before. 'Dolon the Dishonourable' is a firm favourite amongst Om-ba-Don parents. 'Squirt the Flameless' has proved popular with sleepy dragonlets for many generations. Young Trolles are encouraged to emulate the perserverance of 'Clog' who was set the task of capturing his own reflection and who, as is often the way with Trolles, shocked everyone when it seemed he had succeeded. They did not know that Clog was one of a pair of identical twins.

Popular though these stories are — I admit to still enjoying them myself — two characters stand apart from the rest. It has been impossible for me to trace the histories of either: their roots go back so far that even the earliest Krystonian writings mention them. They are extremes. One is good: the other undoubtably evil.

Poppa Lupu visits every dwelling in Krystonia, no matter how humble, on the eve of winter's beginning and, unseen, dispenses small gifts. It is said that even N'Borg awakes to find a small present at the foot of his bed! Though many have tried, nobody has actually seen Poppa Lupu clearly. It seems he sends a strong enchantment before him which makes sleep impossible to resist. Descriptions of him are vague, half-remembered dreams of a portly, bewhiskered spellmaker who chuckles incessantly as he passes from dwelling to dwelling. How he manages to visit every household in the course of a single night has long been the cause for debate in The Obelisk, and many of the Apprentices, determined to prove they are growing intellectually as well as physically, have dismissed Poppa Lupu as a myth, claiming that the gifts left for them have been placed, whilst they snore, by The Council. Of course, The Council denies such interference and Turfen, who specializes in sleep-magic, has often given lectures on the subject. He claims that the explanation is really very simple. Using a spell of greater potency than any known spellcaster could shape, Poppa Lupu causes a brief, but complete suspension of time. As time itself stands still, Poppa Lupu is free to move unhurriedly about his business. Thankfully, the Bahl Witch cannot exert such strong sorcery.

The Bowl of Munn is little more than a depression, as though, at some time long past, a huge ball of rock had fallen from the sky and smashed into the ground. But whilst the crater still exists there is no sign of the ball, and The Obelisk have long since rejected this as a satisfactory theory to explain Munn's creation.

The bowl itself is treeless; the dusty soil supporting only scrubby, gnarled shrubs which never flower. Near the crater's base a series ofl small caves yawn black. It is deep within these that the Bahl Witch is said to preside over a pack of voracious, foul-smelling bonesnappers.

Protected by a spell-shield, Graffyn has ventured into the bowl and right up to the caves themselves. He saw nothing to support or refute the Witch's existence. Yet he could not bring himself to poke so much as a whisker into the caves themselves.

"When you have worked magic for as long as I have you get a feeling, almost a taste when something is awry. I knew that this was a bad place, a source of evil. All the time I was there, I could feel black words reaching out, probing the extent of my power as though searching for a weakness. And I was watched. Though I caught not the smallest gleam of an eye, I knew my every movement was being observed. There was a smell too, bitter and sulphurous that burned in my nose and throat. It is a bad, bad place and no mistake. I was more than a little relieved when I left."

I am sure the Witch would not have taken kindly to Graffyn snooping about her home territory and, had he not been suitably protected, would have done more than just watch him. But, being an adult, Graffyn has nothing to fear when she leaves her caves and goes riding in the night. Astride one of the bonesnappers, she will leap over the sleeping traveller and pass onward without turning one of his whiskers. The Bahl Witch searches for younger victims. For reasons I do not really comprehend, she desires only children!

Perhaps you have noticed, I write of this particular member of the Thane-Keld with more certainty and less doubt than I have written of others. Though many adults are quick to blame her influence for causing their children troubled sleep or bad behaviour just before bedtime, they do not really believe. Her name is used lightly, as a threat. "Go to sleep. Tuck up your fingers and toes. If the Bahl Witch comes a-riding here tonight she is sure to carry such a naughty child away. She likes nothing more than a nice, fat, naughty child!" It pains me when I hear parents say such things, no matter how well-intended they might be. I tell you, the Bahl Witch is no figment of a child's imagination. She exists. I know. I have seen her. She cares not whether her victim is good or bad; only that they are very young.

Contrary to popular opinion she does not steal children from their beds by sending her bonesnappers through any window whose shutters have been left open. If this were true, half the children in Krystonia would vanish on a warm night! No, she is far more devious. Locked shutters and doors are no barrier to her.

Some infants have the unfortunate habit of walking in their sleep. These are the ones who are most at risk and who should be watched. The Bahl Watch disrupts their sleep by sending nightmares and then deceives their slumber-numbed minds, often by imitating the voice of one of their parents. The child, still bound in dreams, hears its parent urging them to rise from their beds and go outside.

"Come! Come! The stars shine so brightly! Come, play outside where the grass is wet with dew. Come, my lovely, come!"

Fortunately her magic is quite weak and her spell easily broken by a stubbed toe, a creaking door that alerts the parents or some other occurrence that breaks the veil of shallow dreams in which her chosen victim is held.

By my escape was due more to good fortune than any disturbance to the Witch's spell.

I recollect sneaking silently past the curtain separating my parents bed from my own. I knew what I was doing but not why I was doing it. I had to go outside. Something was drawing me on, calling me in such a way that I no longer owned a will of my own.

Carefully, I stole to the door and was in the process of sliding back the wooden latch, when I chanced to see a sprig of crimson fire-berries I had picked for my mother earlier in the day. I know not why, but I picked the twig up before slipping out.

Oh, the horror! The Bahl-Witch is as ugly and disformed as she is evil. Her skin hangs loosely in folds about her face. Her toothless mouth is moist. About her, eyes as red as dying suns, the bonesnappers skulk, jaws agape. Their stench is almost as bad as their looks are fierce: and they move on silent paws; their front legs powerful in contrast to their slight hindquarters, giving them a peculiar, stooped, cowling appearance. By some signal from their mistress they drew closer, salivating, eyeing me greedily.

Yet they did not seize me. Upon seeing the fire berries they shrank back, snapping and snarling and would not approach nearer, no matter how their evil queen raged and hissed at them.

"Drop them, my lovely. Throw away those awful berries. They are poison," the Witch entreated. Then, seeing my reluctance, began shrieking. "Drop them! I command it!"

I could not. My hand refused to loosen, and gripped the twig still more tightly. Then I fainted.

Imagine my father's surprise when he discovered his only son lying on the doorstep, clutching a sprig of fire-berries, apparently deep in a blissful sleep.

When he woke me I clung to him fit to choke off his breath.

"What's this?" he laughed. "Have you been out stargazing?"

I tried to tell him about the Witch, and described the bonesnappers in great detail, but he only shook his head and scruffed my hair and laughed.

"What stories you tell," he smiled, carrying me back into the house. "You could make a career out of it and no mistake."

CONFLICT CONTINUED

Since the battle for possession of the Dom Krystal when his magic was thwarted and his legions put to rout, N'Borg has not launched any further direct attacks against The Obelisk. Wisely, The Council did not see this as a final victory or as cowardice on the part of the Dark Lord. Too many of us remember that he stood firm upon the battleground, whilst all about him his legions fled in disarray, squealing back to the Waste of Shugg, to entertain so foolish a notion. Failure will have increased his desire for vengeance as much as it will have taught him caution. Rueggan is not alone in the belief that we now live under the threat from an adversary grown doubly dangerous and determined, and that, one day, we must surely face him again.

In the meantime, N'Borg is proving as artful as he is evil. He concentrates on easier targets — isolated settlements too small or too remote to sustain a resident spellcaster, or races who have not yet sworn fealty to the Great Design — using the threat of force to bring them under his control. Any who resist are dealt with by bloodthirsty Snords and Honji warriors. Those who succumb are subjected to an intense period of 'mind manipulation'. Once complete, all their thoughts and actions are no longer their own and they begin to slide into a darkness from which few have ever been known to return, rejoicing in spiteful acts and foul deeds.

Of late, rather too many have been recruited to take the Path Into Darkness for The Council to ignore. Wherever possible, extra spellcasters have been sent forth to try and protect vulnerable locations. but the effort involved has proven taxing on krystal stocks. N'Borg, having failed to break the heart of the Great Design, is now chipping away at its edges, spreading his evil influence like a malignant tumour, growing stronger at our expense. So wide has his web of corruption become, even the major routes through Keldorran are no longer as safe as they once were.

Mugrahs have never been the sort to invite home to dinner. It takes the slightest excuse to set them spitting, cursing and fighting. They only laugh — a raucous, braying sound that is most unkind on the ear — when it is at someone else's expense and, should the tables be turned, instantly resort to more fist waving and threats. They are small minded, bad mannered and untrustworthy, yet, until quite recently, highly predictable and easy to outwit. In much the same way as a thunderstorm might break a journey and cause some small inconvenience, Mugrahs were just one of those things which had to be endured.

Down from trees they would swing, out of bushes they would jump, landing (ungracefully) on the pathway and intertwining their long arms to form a barrier to prevent their victims from going any further. Next they would start whooping and spitting at the travellers in a terrifying display designed to scare them witless. Unfortunately — for the Mugrahs that is — most of the journeymen were so accustomed to these interruptions they would shrug, roll their eyes and wait patiently for the would-be thieves to calm down. Outraged by their lack of effect, the Mugrahs invariably began to bicker between themselves. Now it only remained for the travellers to throw a tightly tied bag to one side of the path and continue on their way, leaving the Mugrahs to contest ownership of the prize. Although they would bash and bruise each other to within a whisker of consciousness the victor usually discovered he had won a bagfull of stones or grass for his pains. Incredibly, they never seemed to learn from their mistakes and, I have heard how, some travellers began to feel so sorry for the Mugrah's lack of competence they actually stuffed the bag with cakes or sweetened roots.

Now things are different.

N'Chakk, chief executor of most of N'Borg's wicked schemes, found the Mugrahs delightfully easy prey. A sackful of doctored cakes liberally dosed with sleeping powder, a few carefully chosen spell-words whispered into their ears as they lay snoring, and N'Chakk's mission was complete. The Mugrahs awoke changed.

They were still greedy and attracted to a life of robbery, but now their activities began to take on a more sinister edge. They grew stealthier, more cunning, and armed themselves with long, spiked, wooden cludgels. They lay in wait for travellers, nursing an overwhelming desire for revenge. N'Chakk had 'enlightened' them; told the sleeping Mugrahs how everyone laughed and thought them stupid.

"What's the difference between a Mugrah and a large rock? It's more difficult to outwit the rock!"

Their new master valued them, respected their way of life. If only they dispossessed all travellers of any krystal they might be carrying, and sent it to the Krak, the Great One would see to it that nobody would dare laugh at them again. Of course, whatever they decided to do with what was left —the victims included — was their business; although, by way of showing his appreciation, N'Borg had several copies of 'Thirty Ways to Treat Captives' and 'Torture for Beginners' should they wish to develop their skills. (The offer was a barely disguised insult had the Mugrahs the wit to see it. N'Chakk knew they were more likely to know how to fly than they were to read!)

At first their attacks were sporadic — a report that someone had failed to return home at the expected time, or the discovery of a beast of burden running loose in the forest without any owner in attendance — but soon they escalated to a point whereby travellers were banding together and arming themselves before risking negotiating the major forest trade routes. Much krystal was lost, several pitched battles fought, and fatalities recorded on both sides as a result.

The Obelisk responded quickly by allocating a team of young but adept wizards to act as escorts providing magical protection, but the cost in krystal power rapidly outstripped any gains and, finally, they had no choice but to reduce the frequency of escorted passages to a minimum. The traders, particularly those of an opportunistic nature, began to use other, lesser known routes.

For a while they escaped detection and the flow of vital krystal was resumed. N'Borg, however, seeing that his supply had dwindled, sent N'Chakk (and various other spies) out to reverse the situation.

The forest is full of careless mouths. It took no time at all before N'Chakk had learned what he needed to know and, once again, he managed to exploit his knowledge, meeting with scant resistance.

Since a time before time, the Wood-Sprites have inhabited the ancient trees of Keldorran, steadfastly refusing to have anything to do with affairs outside their own secretive community. By day, they occupy the branches of the tallest trees, only descending to the forest floor when night steals between the tree trunks and the stars glimmer in the sky. Then they speak of what they have seen in the course of the day's passing. Hardly a leaf is turned in the breeze, hardly a footfall cracks a twig without their marking the movement. Only the birds, who rarely choose to speak in the Common-Tongue, know more about the comings and going of Keldorran.

The relationship with The Obelisk of this little-known race has always been curteous but formal. It was generally held that the privacy of the Wood-Sprites should be respected until such a time that they themselves chose to come forward. They offered no threat and it appeared more constructive in the long term to leave them to their own devices.

Sadly, what N'Borg and his followers know about respecting the privacy of others could be written on a leafbug's leg. As soon as he became aware of the existence of the Wood-Sprites, N'Chakk saw another wonderful opportunity to interfere in the natural scheme of things and increase his favour with N'Borg. (Ever since the Battle for the Dom, when he had attempted to turn his master's defeat to his own advantage — and was found out — N'Chakk has had to work overtime to avoid being reduced to a pile of ashes).

For some time he set spies to watch the Wood-Sprites, looking for a way to exploit them in the same way he had the

Mugrahs. He soon found their point of vulnerability, and struck.

There is a flower which blooms throughout every season, except winter, upon the Yutop tree. The flowers are exquisitely scented and laden with nectar which attracts many winged bugs. The Wood-Sprites love and revere these flowers, for their fragrance brings sweet dreams of a visionary nature: dreams of another world to which the Wood-Sprites believe they truly belong and to which they will one day return as inheritors.

First N'Chakk summoned a swarm of stinging flies to drive off all the other winged bugs and to make sure the Wood-Sprites were not likely to overlook his actions. Next, he summoned the swarm about him whilst he carefully emptied the contents of a small container onto a square of black fabric. In turn, each fly picked up a single grain of the coarse powder and returned to the Yutop flowers, depositing their minute burdens deep within the whorl of petals. His work complete, N'Chakk and his attendant swarm retired to watch and wait.

What dreams the Wood-Sprites endured after inhaling the poisoned flowers' fragrance, only they can tell. I can only say that the unfortunate Sprites awoke without truly awaking again. Their minds now held different visions than they had previously, but they knew this not. All memory of their former state was lost. They now only wished to serve the desires of he they called The Great One.

"Look how beautiful we've become!" they enthused. "How fair our skin! How green our hair! Praise to the Great One!"

Of course, their eyes were playing tricks upon them. As is usual with any who serve N'Borg, they were altered physically as well as mentally. What they now believed to be beauty was ugliness. Their limbs became deformed, their countenances twisted, their nails long and curved. With the Sprites as his servants, little could pass beneath the green canopy of Keldorran which did not reach the ears of N'Borg and, as before, travellers taking krystal through the forest were invariably waylaid by gangs of Mugrahs who appeared to possess foreknowledge of their chosen routes, regardless of how quietly they moved, or how different the paths they walked.

Where a group of traders did manage to give the Mugrahs the slip, the Sprites themselves would harass and harangue them, worrying the beasts, scratching faces with their sharp little nails whenever the travellers passed beneath low branches, or pelting them with fruits and nuts.

I daresay that N'Borg sat gloating over these minor victories, congratulating himself for the speed and ease with which he had managed to stir up the once peaceful forest. Well, if he did, his smile would not have been half so broad if he had known then what his actions had caused. Admittedly, he had made things uncomfortable but, as is often the case, what he took from one hand was given back in the other. The brightest krystals are often found when you're up to your ears in mud, as they say.

Their quiet lives disrupted by the thuggery of the Mugrahs and the spiteful antics of the Wood-Sprites, some hitherto retiring races approached The Council asking for advice and help. Of these, the Poolahs proved themselves more useful than we could have hoped.

Poolahs are shy, gentle creatures, distantly related to the Bobolls of the Kappah. They are small, little more than chest height to a Trolle when fully grown, have enormous, doleful eyes, exemplary manners and selfless hearts. Most remarkable of all are their eyebrows. When young these are little more than prominent, bushy outgrowths but, as they mature, the eyebrows continue to sprout, becoming a thick, luxuriant growth which, in some of the most ancient members of their race, are so long they are either tied or held up to prevent their owner from becoming tangled or tripping over. They know the location of every single forest path, down to the last twist and turn. Best of all, they, like so many of the most gentle races, possess their own, unique magic.

Though their knowledge of the Common-Tongue is, yet, quite limited, the Poolahs can converse fluently with any beast of fur and feather. The birds, who frequently enjoy titbits at their table, speak freely of all they have seen or heard. The Bush-Tailed Nutlings which scamper along aeriel highways of intertwined branches and chatter in alarm whenever a strange face is seen in the forest, bring the Poolahs nuts and berries along with news of unusual events. Able to glean such information, the Poolahs were more than willing to share it with representatives from The Obelisk; particularly as The Council generously donated several spell-charged krystals that warded off the Mugrahs who had begun to turn to Poolah-hunting whenever highway robbery was not available.

With the Poolah's assistance, The Council had been given the means to begin countering the depredations of the Mugrah gangs and the Wood-Sprites. Flocks of birds swoop down, pecking and beating with their wings, whenever the Wood-Sprites are located, chasing them back into hollows and knots, and then confining them to their bolt holes by perching within easy striking distance. The Nutlings, thoroughly enjoying the opportunity to make a nuisance of themselves and get rewarded for their trouble, seek out the Mugrahs and follow them, chattering wildly, betraying their presence to any travellers. These mischievous little creatures have so entered into the spirit of the game — for a game is all it is to them — they even interrupt sleeping Mugrahs in the dead of night by chattering and raining dead twigs down upon them. This has proved an extremely effective tactic. Mugrahs who have spent a restless night invariably oversleep and awake after the traders have long since passed. Even those possessing the wherewithall to use earplugs soon regret their decision. While they sleep the Nutlings sneak down from the trees and pour resin into their ears. Come the morning, the Mugrahs are far too busy trying to unstop them to think about attacking travellers!

The knowledge which the Poolahs glean from the birds has also proved invaluable to me when compiling accurate accounts for entry onto my parchment. By and large, it seems birds are regarded as being as much a part of the scenery as a tree or a rock. Whilst I have often seen participants of private meeting search every surrounding tree and check behind every rock before beginning to speak openly of their business, I have never seen one pay the slightest attention to the bird which pecked in the soil at their feet. Birds have a phenomenal talent for mimicry, and many are capable of repeating a conversation so accurately that they even reproduce accent and dialect to a degree of perfection whereby the identity of the speakers are known! It is they, not I, who should be thanked for many of the details contained in my chronicles. Without them, what follows would be either supposition or damagingly biased. As it is, I present what I believe to be true reportage.

A NARROW SQUEAK

Ah, there you are," murmured N'Borg, without turning from the narrow slot window set into the wall of his private chamber. He continued watching the Honji warrior in the courtyard below putting a patrol of Snords through their paces. The Dark Lord exuded an air of indifference close to boredom.

"I came as soon as I received your summons, Great One." The black-robed spellcaster bowed, then stood, waiting silently with the same kind of nervous agitation one sometimes sees in a maltreated beast at the approach of its owner. It was obvious he would sooner be anywhere else.

"Of course you did," the Dark Lord replied, sardonically. He turned and fixed his inferior with an unwavering stare, at once heightening the tension in the room. "Of course you did."

"May I ask what the Great One desires of his humble servant?"

N'Borg's eyes narrowed and his lips tightened to form a sneer. "Humble servant? Ha! When are you going to tire of these petty games N'Chakk? When next will you try and seat yourself on my throne?"

"My Lord! How could you ever think . . ."

"You forget yourself, N'Chakk. I do not think, I *know!* I have read and remembered every thought that has ever crossed your treacherous mind. Do not insult me by such shows of feigned loyalty. You serve from fear, that is all."

A flicker of anger flashed momentarily in N'Chakk's eyes, but he had grown familiar with N'Borg's abrasive manner and immediately subdued his desire to respond. His face quickly acquired its usual half-smile, half-sneer.

"I have been looking over your accounts of my stock of krystal," continued N'Borg, turning back to the window. He paused, as though expecting N'Chakk to offer some reply, but the only sound to disturb the cold air of the room came from outside where the Honji's whip cracked. This was followed, almost instantly, by a howl of pain from the Snord whose rump had received the lash.

"Perhaps you would care to explain why, when I add what has come in to what I already held, and make allowances for any used, I am found wanting?" He paused briefly before continuing. "My accounting differs from yours. When I visited the strongroom my eyes told a different story than did your ledgers."

"I am currently investigating the matter," N'Chakk replied, trying to sound reassuring.

"Then I would not discover the shortfall were I to order a search of your quarters?"

"My Lord!" exclaimed N'Chakk, indignantly. "Send your personal bodyguard to my rooms this moment! Any use I have made of krystal has been sanctioned by yourself."

N'Borg knew that, for once, N'Chakk was speaking the truth, but he enjoyed the discomfort his insinuations caused too much to left the opportunity be wasted.

"So explain," N'Borg demanded. "You are charged with the responsibility for security, are you not?"

"I can assure my lord that I am hopeful of bringing the culprit before you in the very near future."

"Let us hope it is before my tolerance and patience runs out," N'Borg threatened.

"My Lord shall not have long to wait," promised N'Chakk, bowing and backing towards the doorway as he did so.

"I'd better not," finished N'Borg. "I do not really want to appoint N'Grall to head the inquiry. He is far too busy and valuable to waste doing jobs others should have done for themselves."

"Of course. It will not be necessary to trouble N'Grall," N'Chakk assured, shuffling backwards out into the corridor.

Once out of sight of N'Borg, N'Chakk straightened, assuming the disdainful, erect posture he displayed before all the other occupants of Krak N'Borg. He spat vehemently. How he detested having to bow and scrape. He detested the idea of N'Grall taking over the charge of the krystal cache even more.

The very notion of the Henchdragon's supercillious attitude if he thought he had succeeded in usurping N'Chakk filled the black spellmaster with anger. He had recognised N'Borg's deliberate barb in mentioning N'Grall's name, and the very fact that the Dark Lord had known it would sting, irked him still more. Somewhere, deep within, N'Chakk harboured a creeping fear of the dragon's power and quick mind. He hated N'Borg; he hated N'Grall; he hated every piece of this cold and dismal place, down to the last stone. Only the thought that it would fall into his grasp in the fullness of time stopped him from deserting the Waste of Shugg forever. In the meantime, he had better solve the mystery of the disappearing krystals. There was no sense in making things any more uncomfortable for himself than they already were.

To N'Chakk's chagrin, his careful questioning and outright threats failed to reveal the identity of the krystal thief. He had half suspected the Snords who stood guard outside the strongroom, though found it hard to think what possible use such mudwits could find for the powerful stones. Still, he had them stretched, whipped and pegged out in the snow to make him feel better. One of the Snords, after being hung by the heels and tickled senseless, finally confessed but, on the very night of his arrest, several more krystals were missing. N'Chakk had the Snord tickled again for timewasting, ranted and raged at the guards until he was hoarse, and then retired to his quarters to think. There must be some way of snaring the thief and salvaging his damaged reputation. Already the Honji were making sly comments whenever they thought his back was turned.

Many candles later, N'Chakk suddenly thumped the arm of his chair. There could be only one explanation: magic! Some enchantment must be at work which tricked, or deceived the eyes of those stupid Snord guards!

He was almost right. There was a magic of sorts at work, but not of the kind he suspected. The Snords were under no enchantment. They, like most of us, cannot know what they cannot see.

If you are already familiar with the Bobolls' fondness for 'zumping' then you should be excused the following explanation. But for the enlightenment of those who have never before encountered the Snow-Sprites, or know of their peculiar gift, I offer a brief account.

A Boboll can, merely by thinking, vanish from under your nose and reappear in a flash some distance away. This is a 'zump'. They have little control over the location of their materialisation and sometimes perform three or four successive zumps before they find themselves where they want to be. Though no spell words or krystal power is involved, the trick does require considerable expenditure of energy on the Bobolls' part and, after a series of zumps, the little creatures can become so exhausted they fall asleep on their feet and need a rest before they can zump again. However, beyond these limitations, a Bobbol is nigh impossible to catch.

Since they were kits the size and colour of a snowball, Poffles and Trumph have used their ability to zump to the full, outwitting Myzer by zumping through the wall of his fortified cabin and out again with an armful of his precious krystals. By the time they reached maturity (if such a term can ever be applied to any Bobbol!) Poffles and Trumph were krystal stealers of reputation; between them accounting for almost a twentieth of all new krystal received by The Obelisk in any one season. I suppose it was inevitable that they would one day turn their attentions to the largest single krystal collection outside The Council —N'Borg's cache in the Krak N'Borg.

Their first attempt is written in detail in earlier Chronicles. Enough for me to say here is that they escaped by the narrowest of squeaks with nothing but their own skins and returned to their holts on the snowline of Kappah vowing never to go back to the Waste of Shugg again.

For a while they were as good as their word and confined their activities to plundering Myzer's krystal hoard as previously but, unfortunately, the Bobolls — and these two in particular — are prone to sudden memory lapses when it suits them.

Growing bored with filching from their old adversary, they decided only the Krak offered a fitting test of their talent as sneak thieves. The dire threat of the Dark Lord's stronghold was more than compensated for by the size of the krystal collection he held under lock and key. Where, exactly, the strongroom was located, they were unsure, but it would be worth a second visit to the Krak if only to relieve the boredom of robbing Myzer.

Thus they vanished from their holts early in the Season of the Reawakening and did not return until long after the mountain meadows were full of flowers. This time they returned dragging a large cloth bag behind them. To The Council's delight, it was full of the most high quality spell krystal imaginable, and almost compensated completely for the krystal which had been lost to the Mugrahs!

After being treated to a platter full of Hotpottle's finest sweet cakes, and giving a useful and very detailed report of the Krak's internal layout, the two Bobolls returned to their homes for a long, well-earned rest.

They slept for three days and, when they eventually awoke, spent another three stuffing themselves with so much food it was a wonder they did not burst. So taut was Trumph's belly, the patch of naked skin in the middle of his stomach was almost twice its usual size and, when Poffles hit it with a twig, sounded like a drum.

On the seventh day they disappeared again.

In the interim, N'Chakk had discovered the shortfall in the Krystal stocks, had his ear bent by N'Borg, and decided that some magic was responsible. So it was that when Poffles and Trumph stood before the ventilation flue through which they got into the Krak (the walls being too thick to zump through) N'Chakk had tightened security and begun to formulate a plan to counteract the magic he believed to be afoot.

On the first night, Poffles and Trumph had a more difficult time than they had previously. There were Snords everywhere and they had to zump so many times to avoid detection they barely had energy left to escape. They buried the krystals in the snow outside and, too tired to look for anywhere else, dug little snow pits in which to sleep.

As they slept N'Chakk once more discovered krystal missing. For a while he vented his anger and frustration on the guards but, as he returned to his quarters, something caught his eye. Snagged on the edge of a protruding stone block, a small wisp of white fur fluttered in the draught that ran through all the corridors in the grim stronghold. N'Chakk bent down and pulled it free, holding the fur between a thumb and finger. It felt soft, warm, and he knew it did not belong to any of the Krak's inhabitants. Yet there was something familiar about it; a feeling that he had seen such fur before and should recognize it. He walked on to his room, deep in thought. Missing krystals and now this. There had to be some connection.

That night, while N'Chakk sat thinking, Poffles and Trumph returned. This time they had devised a plan to make their entry into the strongroom a little easier. Carrying a few small stones they threw them down the corridor in which the Snords stood. Hearing the clatter on the stone floor, the dim-witted guards ran to investigate, leaving the door unattended. Whilst they were facing away, waving their torches and grunting in excitement, Poffles and Trumph sneaked behind them and zumped through the door. Once more they plundered the heap of Krystals and zumped their way back to safety outside.

The next night was to be very different.

N'Chakk awoke, huddled beneath his blankets, to receive news of the latest robbery. He merely grunted and dismissed the Honji without taking his head off the pillow. He may as well stay abed until he thought of something positive to do. Besides his knee was aching as it always did on very cold mornings . . .

He was out of bed and on his feet in an instant, calling for his servant to bring his robes! Of course! That was it! Now he remembered!

In the midst of the offensive against the cursed do-gooders he had noticed little white creatures which plagued the advancing Snords by nipping their ankles and fingers. What was most remarkable was the way they vanished before a blow could be struck against them. N'Chakk himself had been bitten just above the knee and it had troubled him ever since. The white fur in the corridor . . . it just had to be! . . .

N'Chakk had not been spared after his attempt to persuade N'Grall to desert his master and serve with him because N'Borg valued his company. In truth, they each detested the sight of the other. N'Borg had declined taking revenge because of N'Chakk's usefulness. He was an extremely adept and powerful spellcaster who could accomplish more with a few words of magic than a legion of Snords could by brute force. It was magic that N'Chakk would use to snare the krystal thief once and for all.

Poffles and Trumph were both a little surprised to find the Snord guard not as heavy as it had been before, but they did not stop to question why this should be so. If it made it easier to get into the strongroom, then so much the better. It was not long before they were happily rummaging through the krystals, picking out only the most perfect and flawless examples.

"Not quite as exciting as we thought it would be, is it?" whispered Trumph. "I don't think N'Borg's as all powerful and clever as the wizards say he is."

"Not clever enough to catch a Boboll anyway," giggled Poffles.

They would soon regret their words.

When Poffles and Trumph tried to zump out of the strongroom they were shocked and surprised to find they could not. They heard the same sort of wind noise which always filled their ears prior to a zump, but it was cut short by a loud bang and a thump on their heads as though they had collided with some solid, inpenetrable barrier. They tried again and again, but each time they opened their eyes to find themselves still inside the strongroom, and they were both soon suffering from awful headaches.

"Keep trying," urged Poffles, "there must be a hole somewhere!"

If there was a hole in N'Chakk's spell wall, the Bobolls could not find it. Had they had the good sense to save themselves until someone opened the door, they might have fared better, but so scared were they, the Bobolls tried zump after useless zump until they collapsed in a heap on the krystals and fell sound asleep, their power completely exhausted.

That was how N'Chakk found them the next morning, cuddled together on top of the heap of krystals.

"Look what we have here," he pronounced triumphantly, for the benefit of the Snords, "not one, but two little thieves!"

Poffles and Trumph continued snoring, oblivious to everything.

"Bring them to the deep chambers for interrogation," he ordered. He would pick their brains himself before letting N'Borg know of their capture. Perhaps they might have some useful information?

The Snords pulled the sleeping Bobolls from the room, dragging them along the corridor by the heels. Once or twice the Bobolls groaned as their heads banged against the cold stones, but they slept on, in their dreams interpreting the blows as another failed attempt to escape from the strongroom.

Throughout N'Chakk's interrogation they regained consciousness only momentarily and, no matter how he had them tickled or stretched on the rack, N'Chakk left them knowing nothing more than the names of several types of mountain flowers and a list of Trumph's favourite foods. He would see them again later when they were properly awake and unable to resist his tortures. In the meanwhile, they were thrown into a miserable dungeon which N'Chakk had sealed with a spell to prevent their zumping out.

The Bobolls awoke huddled in a corner on a pile of decomposing grass. The smell was disgusting and they both wrinkled up their noses.

"Phew!" Trumph exclaimed. "You stink!"

"You don't smell so sweet yourself," Poffles retorted.

"Hey! You look like you've grown!" Trumph observed.

Poffles looked down at himself. "I feel like I have," he replied. "My bones are aching as though they've been stretched."

*Caught at last! Poffles and Trumph won't be able to 'zump' their way out of this fix . . . will
they?*

Of course, the next thing they did was to try zumping, but they ended up on the wet floor, holding their heads.

"The next time I say anything about excitement give me a good kick," groaned Trumph.

"Har! Har! We've gottcha now and no mistake!"

Poffles and Trumph could just make out the warty snout and wicked little eyes of a Snord poking through a small square in the heavy door.

"Get lost hogface!" shouted Poffles.

"And fetch us something to eat!" demanded Trumph.

"Oh, I am sorry," replied the Snord in a wheedling voice, "but you were asleep when dinner was served and I didn't want to wake you, so I ate it! Har! Har!"

The Snord's face vanished, leaving the two Bobolls miserable and wet, wondering what to do next. They were in a fix now and no mistake.

For a while, they poked around the small dungeon but, apart from a few old bones and a set of manacles, they found nothing to offer comfort, or anything remotely edible. They slumped down on the stinking grass and waited.

They did not have long to wait before a key was turned in the lock and heavy, stiff bolts were drawn back.

"Put these on!" snapped the Snord goaler, throwing a set of heavy manacles at them. "One on each, that way you can't try anything."

Poffles and Trumph did as they were told and shuffled out of the dungeon, one leg and one arm fastened to each other, dragging the chain across the floor.

"Oh yeah," the Snord added, poking them in the shoulders with a pointed stick to make them hurry, "they found where you hid the krystals earlier so yer mates won't be coming back to collect anything except your bones. Har! Har!"

"We came alone," protested Poffles.

"Tell that to 'is Greatness," grunted the Snord, giving them both another poke with the stick. "He'll have the truth out of yah one way or the other before long."

N'Chakk was waiting in the torture chamber when Poffles and Trumph were thrust through the door and given a final prod by their goaler.

"Isn't that the one whose knee you bit?" hissed Poffles under his breath.

Trumph gulped and nodded.

"My friends!" N'Chakk cackled. "So glad you could join me. I thought you might like to see some of the attractions of our humble home that will be used for your . . . how shall I say? . . . yes, your entertainment!" N'Chakk laughed and, outside the door, Poffles and Trumph could hear that the Snord was obviously amused by the amount of "Har-Hars" he was making. "Here we have the rack for stretching," continued N'Chakk, stroking the wooden frame fondly. "And here is the wheel. Over there is the tickling frame and the hot mud bath. To your left, the bed of spikes and, to your right, my particular favourite, the pit full of ever-hungry beasties. Quite a choice, don't you think?"

The Bobolls said nothing.

"Of course, you can avoid sampling these delights if you choose to tell me everything, and I mean everything, you know about The Council of Wizards and The Obelisk.

Poffles and Trumph were so frightened they went into an involuntary zump which nearly wrenched their limbs from their sockets.

N'Chakk seemed extremely amused by this. "I'm glad to see that you will now have noticed I took the precaution of laying a holding spell upon your fetters in case you decided to attempt using your trickery to escape." He laughed again before becoming suddenly serious and threatening. "You have until nightfall to decide. By then the mud bath should have warmed nicely."

"Go and eat your beard!" Poffles retorted. "We'll tell you nothing!"

"We shall see," hissed N'Chakk. "Guard!"

The Snord clattered through the door. "Yes sir?"

"Take the prisoners back to their dungeon. They are to

receive no food or drink. Bring them back at nightfall to begin questioning.'

"Very good sir!" replied the Snord, before jabbing the stick into Trumph's bare midriff. "Right you two, get moving!"

"We're up to our ears in trouble this time," said Trumph glumly, when they were back in the dungeon. "I'm going to die on an empty stomach."

"Perhaps not," said Poffles thoughtfully.

"What? Do you think they'll waste food on us? Not likely, I'm sure."

"Stop twittering on about the state of your belly," said Poffles. "If you used your head as much as your stomach we'd soon be out of here."

"Alright," retorted Trumph, "seeing that you're so smart, you get us out of here."

"I will," replied Poffles, confidently.

"How?"

"Don't ask, just do exactly what I say when I say. Understand?"

"Not really," Trumph commented. "What are you going to do?"

"There are too many ears in this place for talking freely," Poffles observed, nodding towards the door. The Snord's snout was poking through again.

"Looking forward to this evening I hope," he grunted. "I am! Har! Har!"

"Drop dead warty," replied Poffles. "Remember," he whispered to Trumph, "Do exactly what I say."

It seemed no time at all before the Snord returned to escort them back to the torture chamber. As before he threw the manacles into the dungeon and waited whilst Poffles secured them.

"Wait a fleabite," he snuffled as they shuffled out. "Don't think you'll fool me that easily." He tugged at the clasps to make sure they were closed properly. "Ah ha! Just as I thought. Someone didn't shut them tight, did they now." He snapped the fastener on Poffles wrist shut.

"Oh dear!" whined Trumph. "We've had it now."

"A hot bath for you two, Har! Har! Can't fool old Fester so easy as that. Been in this game too long, so I have."

Once again, the Snord poked and prodded the Bobolls along the labyrinth of corridors and towards the chamber. Past the rows of ventilation flues that brought the clean, cold smell of outside to their noses they went, Poffles slowly getting his bearings, Trumph on the verge of tears.

"Remember what I told you?" asked Poffles at length.

"Shurrup! No talking!" oinked the Snord.

"Yes," replied Trumph, ignoring the order.

"Oi! Shurrup I tell you!" This time the Snord jabbed Trumph viciously.

"When I say zump, I mean zump," Poffles continued.

"What! We can't ... "

"Do as I say," Poffles reiterated, just before he too was poked sternly in the back.

"One ... two ... three ... ZUMP!"

The Snord had lunged forward to jab his stick in Trumphs rear, but neither his rear, or any other part of him was there, and the Snord fell, face down, bruising his snout and cursing loud enough to bring the walls down.

"Oi! Come back 'ere!" he bellowed, entangled in the empty manacles.

"Har! Har!" replied two small voices. "Har! Har!"

Whether Fester the Snord jailer was used as a substitute for the two Bobolls in N'Chakk's torture chamber we know not. We do know, however, that N'Borg, upon learning of N'Chakk's incompetence, took the keys to the strongroom from him and gave them to N'Grall. As if this wasn't enough, he also sent N'Chakk out to command a Snord patrol on a 'security tour' of Shugg's freezing outer wastes.

"How did you know the enchantment had worn off?" asked Trumph, as the two Bobolls journeyed back to the Kappah.

"I didn't know if it had or not," replied Poffles. "But then, we weren't wearing the same manacles, so it didn't really matter."

"I still don't understand. I thought when he checked if they were locked that we'd had it."

"I had to let him find something or he would have been even more suspicious. As it was, he thought he'd foiled us."

"I still don't understand," said Trumph, scratching his head.

"Don't you remember that old set of manacles we found in the dungeon? I just swapped one set for the other."

"Ahh! I see! That was pretty clever," Trumph congratulated.

"Thank you," said Poffles, "it makes a change for you to admit it."

"But if you were really, really clever," Trumph added, "you'd be able to find me a big slice of cake."

THE QUEEN BETWEEN WORLDS

Leila was a quiet sort of girl, given to long bouts of deep introspection which others in the settlement of Plumstock saw as detachment and unwillingness to contribute to their small, insular community. Thus, for all the fair looks she possessed as she grew into maidenhood, she never enjoyed the attentions of a suitor and remained unloved long after most of the other maidens had been bethrothed and produced youngsters of their own. With only the dull-witted or wastrel sons of the settlement left unattached, she resigned herself to a future alone, for she was not, as some were, willing to accept what she considered to be second best.

Instead, Leila became yet more aloof and began going off into the forest, enjoying its peace and tranquility after what she saw as the pointless gossiping and petty jealousies of Plumstock society. Besides, if washing, cooking and mending clothes was all there was to life, then she was better off by herself.

Seated beneath a tree, the sun warm on her face and the birds singing above, Leila could indulge in flights of fancy, picturing the strange and wonderful places which lay beyond her normal sight. For her, two worlds existed. She was chained to one by her body, but the other was an altogether better place where the only barriers she knew were those set by the limits of her imagination.

In Leila's better world, flocks of birds would lift her from the ground and take her to wherever she wished to go. The rain was warm and tasted like orchid's dew. The wind laughed aloud as it ran before her. Beneath the surface of a stream lived a Prince and Princess who rode upon the backs of golden fish and wore crowns bejewelled with silver bubbles. Up in the treetops dwelt the King Between Worlds, the master of a realm lying where the land ended and the open sky began. He was handsome, clever and kind, loved by all his subjects. But he was lonely. One day he would see Leila and love her as much as she already loved him, and would come to carry her up into his secret kingdom.

There she would sit by his side and rule as his Queen Between Worlds for ever and ever.

It was always a disappointment when some sound disturbed her daydreams, and even more depressing to return to Plumstock when night fell.

One day, when she was immersed in a particularly vivid fantasy, and the King Between Worlds was just about to whisk her away to eternal happiness, Leila sensed some sudden change in her lesser, mundane world; a disturbance in the usual ambience she strove so hard to escape from. She resisted the insistence of her mind trying to call her back to reality for as long as she could, but when it became obvious the King would never arrive whilst such a background of disquiet existed she opened her eyes, vexed and frustrated.

She gasped, rubbed her eyes, then crept silently behind a low bush. Standing so close she could see every coarse bristle upon the napes of their necks, were a group of Snords, She knew not what they were but, judging by their rank odour and wicked features she instinctively recognised they were no friends. She lay, stock still, listening as the Snords talked amongst themselves.

"It's just over there," said one, pointing vaguely.

"Nah. It's more thataway," replied a second, shaking his tusked snout.

"You're both softer than a tail tassle," grunted a third, impatiently. "Give us the map!" He snatched a piece of parchment from them and began turning it around. "It's over there," he finally pronounced, authoritatively.

"You've got the map upside down you idiot!" interjected another.

"Well, in that case it must be the other way," replied the map reader, obviously annoyed that his decision had been proven incorrect.

"You're all wrong," said another. "We passed the turning a ways back."

Just when it looked as though the Snords were about to decide the matter by fighting it out, one of them suddenly stiffened and began to scent the air, his snout wrinkling as he did so.

"Oi! D'you lot smell summat?" He snuffled loudly, and the others began to follow suit.

"Yeah, you're right an'all. I can smell it now!" agreed another. They all began sniffing loudly.

"A settlement dweller!" confirmed the first Snord. "I'd know that smell anywhere."

"Close by, too," added the second.

Leila all but fainted when she saw them turn until they were facing her but, gathering her wits, she scrambled to her feet and began to run as fast as she could.

"There it goes! After it!" squealed one of the Snords, seeing her break from cover.

Leila ran faster than she would have believed possible, the Snords in hot pursuit, towards Plumstock and safety. Though not so quick across the ground as a Snord, she was more sure of foot and knew the path better than they. Had she not chanced a fleeting glance behind, she might have even outrun them.

Suddenly her foot caught against something and she fell headlong, sprawling face down upon a patch of sponge-plant. But the Snords·did not fall upon her as she had expected. Instead, Leila heard them come to an abrupt halt as another unfamiliar voice spoke out.

"Well now, what's all this?"

"A spy sir," one of the Snords replied, breathlessly.

"Yes sir, a spy sir," the others agreed in chorus.

"A spy, eh?" Leila was pulled up by the arm onto her feet to find N'Chakk's dark eyes regarding her keenly.

"Doesn't look like much of a spy to me," he said. "Much too pretty."

"She was eavesdropping," one of the Snords assured. "She overhead us talking about Plumstock."

N'Chakk's eyebrows lifted slightly and he looked at Leila intensely as though searching her mind. "Did she now? Well, what should I do with you, I wonder?"

"Let me go. I heard nothing!" she protested.

"Poke her eyes out with sticks!" suggested one of the Snords.

"And cut her tongue out!" added another.

"Then roast her slowly over an open fire, basting occasionally. When almost cooked, add a few fresh roots, a pinch of wild spice and brown on a low heat for . . ."

"Shutup!" commanded N'Chakk. "How can I concentrate with you blithering on. You're giving me a headache!"

"He's giving me an appetite," replied one of the Snords, already beginning to salivate.

"The next one of you to make so much as a squeak will be on sentry duty for the rest of the tour!" snapped N'Chakk.

The Snords fell silent, but continued to eye Leila as though she were all but cooked and served. Leila looked away. She had always yearned for excitement, but this was not at all how she had envisioned it. Unless the King Between Worlds made a miraculous appearance it seemed she was destined to end her days as a banquet.

"Go and tell the Honji on the other flank I want to see him immediately," N'Chakk said to the nearest and most hungry-looking Snord. "Tell him all surveillance is cancelled until further notice."

The Snord trotted off whilst his comrades, obviously disappointed, began squabbling, digging each other in the ribs with their elbows and kicking shins when they thought N'Chakk was looking away.

"Bind her," N'Chakk ordered. "But not too tightly, I don't want her bruised more than is necessary."

"So we are going to cook her?" one Snord asked, obviously cheered.

"You disgust me!" spat N'Chakk, disdainfully. "She may be better kept awhile."

"She looks just right for roasting now," one of the Snords observed.

"Quiet you mudwit!" N'Chakk barked. "Can't you see, she might tell us more in a day than we could learn in a season by normal methods."

"She can talk while she's cooking," offered one of the Snords in a last desperate attempt to secure a meal.

"Do as I command!" N'Chakk hissed, running out of patience. "Bind her, then make camp." He pointed to one of the Snords accusingly. "And if I feel so much as a grain of sand in my bedding tonight, it'll be you who's roasted!"

Leila spent the night trussed to a tree in the midst of the encampment. Several times the Snords approached to appraise her fitness for cuisine, getting into several heated discussions over whether the thigh was a superior roast to the calf, or if hot-spice garnish should be preferred to root sauce. Always, either N'Chakk or the Honji officer rebuked them sharply and they withdrew, muttering and chomping their tusks.

She was awoken, stiffened by cold and the tightness of her bonds, by N'Chakk.

"I trust you slept well?" N'Chakk began, half-sneering.

"Can I go now?" Leila asked hopefully.

"I am afraid not. However, I am sending you to a place where you may receive better attention than our humble encampment has offered."

"Where"

"To the home of Great One: Krak N'Borg."

Leila looked terrified. Even in Plumstock they had heard of N'Borg.

"I suggest you are co-operative," advised N'Chakk. "A pretty face won't buy many favours there." He turned and summoned the Honji officer, who marched smartly forward flanked by two Snords.

"Tell the Master I send my greetings and a prisoner who is a native of Plumstock to be interrogated at his leisure. We shall move on to survey Durgen, then onto Kalmuz. I expect to return home with the required information before winter begins."

"Yes sir. The message shall be conveyed," the Honji replied.

"And ensure the maiden is not handled too roughly," warned N'Chakk. "Should you lose her, or should she perish before you reach the Krak, I shall deal with you severely upon my return."

"As you say sir," confirmed the Honji, before yanking Leila to her feet none too gently.

Though Leila's passage to the Waste of Shugg was arduous — due as much to the brutish manners of her escorts as the strains of forced marching upon untrained feet — she still found time to appreciate the variation in the landscapes she encountered, often exclaiming with delight when some new vista unexpectedly presented itself as a feast for her eyes and curiosity. The Snords laughed whenever she showed such wonder and interest, and made references to the view she was destined to enjoy from the inside of a dungeon. The Honji officer merely shook his head, certain the maiden had been touched by madness. Still, she was his ticket for a early return from patrol and he was sensible enough to make sure N'Chakk's orders were obeyed, soon quashing any suggestions from the Snords that she would be less of a burden and they would make faster progress if she were shared equally between their stomachs.

Through it all, Leila could not repress a certain, strange notion that, at long last, life had taken an interesting turn. So what if a dungeon awaited her: it could not be much worse than a daily round of domestic chores in Plumstock. Not once did she experience the smallest twinge of homesickness. If she missed anything at all, it was only the comfort of her warm bed and a hot meal.

Leila's romantic idea was completely dashed the moment she was cast into one of the Krak's dungeons. The stench was unbearable, particularly to one who had spent most of her days in the fragrance-laden air of the forest. Day and night — though these were indistinguishable to Leila — her ears were assailed and her nerves stretched by the shrieks, wails and lamentations of the prisoners in adjacent cells. Everything was damp and covered with mold and slime, and the food, what little she received, was stale and hard enough to break teeth. When a Snord eventually unlocked the cell door and instructed her to follow him to the Great One's chamber, Leila was almost light of spirit. Death would be preferable to another spell in the dungeons.

"Kneel before the Great One!" the Snord ordered, shoving Leila so hard in the back that she had little choice. "The captive sent from Plumstock for interrogation, your Magnificence."

"Wait outside," replied N'Borg, dismissing the Snord with a wave of his hand. Then, turning his attention to the dishevelled girl before him, he was immediately struck, not by her fair looks — she was far too besmirched with dungeon-grime to look her best — but by her attitude. She was kneeling but not, it appeared, with the slightest sign of fear or subordination. If he was not mistaken, she was actually looking about her, as though appraising the fixtures and furnishings of his chamber in a similar manner one might expect from a curious guest entering your home for the first time. This was not at all the sort of behaviour N'Borg was used to!

"Your name?" he asked.

"Leila," she replied, still looking about her.

"From the settlement of Plumstock?"

"Yes."

"Good. You will answer all my questions with equal directness?"

"If you wish," she returned, now looking N'Borg in the eye, "but I would much prefer to sit on that chair while I did so." She nodded towards a richly upholstered chair next to a low table. "My knees are getting cold."

N'Borg almost choked. Who did this girl think she was addressing!

"Answer as you are," he snapped. "Do not try my patience. I have the power of life or death over every living thing within the walls of the Krak, including you."

"Then put me to death if it makes you happy," Leila replied

with a shrug.

"Happy? Happy!" exclaimed N'Borg incredulously. "I try to avoid happiness. It weakens the mind."

"So what reason do you have for doing anything?"

N'Borg open and shut his mouth, momentarily lost for words. At length, having collected his wits, he replied: "Because it brings power, and power is something I do enjoy."

"All seems a bit pointless if you're not happy," Leila said, once more distracted by her surroundings.

"It is I who ask the questions, not you." N'Borg felt as though he were in danger of losing his grip on proceedings.

"As you like," replied Leila, "but I shall sit on the chair if it's no trouble. This floor of yours is really awfully cold. In fact, the whole place would be a great deal pleasanter with a bit of heating." She rose, walked over to the chair and sat down, stroking the padded arms with the tips of her fingers. "Much better," she observed. "Please, continue with your questions. Take as long as you like."

"I think I shall have you killed after all," N'Borg growled threateningly. "You're not taking this at all seriously."

"Then have me killed," Leila replied calmly. "But I must say, I take being kidnapped, dragged from one corner of this land to the other, thrown in the smelliest, dampest dungeon ever built, and then told to kneel on a cold floor very seriously."

"You claim not to fear death?" asked N'Borg, genuinely interested.

"Why should I fear what will come? What matter if it be today? Death is inevitable," Leila concluded, with a sigh of resignation.

"Untrue," N'Borg corrected. "There are those of us who need never feel Death's touch."

Now it was Leila's turn to be interested. "You claim you will never die?"

N'Borg nodded slowly. "Unless my power is taken from me, and, I can promise you, that is extremely unlikely." For some reason, N'Borg found he could not resist the temptation to show off in front of the girl. "My power is greater than any in

Krystonia."

"That's all very good for you Mister N'Borg," Leila replied respectfully, "but I possess no power and know I shall die. Therefore I cannot fear it."

There was a strange logic in the girl's thinking which N'Borg found difficult to grasp. For a moment, N'Borg, like the Honji officer, wondered if Leila was mad. She was either mad or uncommonly clever, he decided.

"Enough," he said, seating himself opposite. "I cannot waste time with smalltalk. Now tell me — and take care to answer truthfully —how much krystal is held in Plumstock at any one time?..."

Leila answered N'Borg's questions honestly. She also asked the Dark Lord several more herself and, without realising it (or, at least, without wanting to admit it to himself) the most evil spellcaster to ever mouth a charm word, and who prided himself on his coldness, talked with a freedom and openness he had never known before. Leila offered no threat. She seemed to seek nothing more than company and conversation and, for the first time in his life, N'Borg experienced something of the pleasure involved in talking about oneself to an appreciative audience. It took the snoring of the Snord outside the door, which had grown increasingly louder, to interrupt them.

"It is time you returned to the dungeons," N'Borg said, determined that Leila should not think she had in any way melted his ice-like personality.

"No! I will not go back there ever again!" she cried, equally determined.

"It is not your place to choose," reminded N'Borg. "You forget yourself too often."

"Then I shall kill myself!" Leila sobbed. "I shall! I shall!" she wailed, growing hysterical.

"But you are a prisoner; an enemy," replied N'Borg, thinking this seemed a perfectly reasonable explanation. "You may try to escape."

"Escape? Me? Where to? How far could I get?" Leila asked,

punctuating each question with a sob. "I have not spoken a single false word to you. Why should you doubt me if I give my word I shall not attempt to escape?"

N'Borg scratched his beard. He had never encountered a co-operative prisoner before and was not at all sure what to do.

"I'll kill myself, I really will!" Leila pressed, sensing N'Borg's uncertainty. "My death will be on your conscience."

N'Borg found the idea that he had a conscience almost humorous — dealing death had been part of his daily activities for as long as he cared to remember — but there was something about the settlement girl he found . . .

"Guard!"

There was a sudden break in the rhythmical snoring outside and, soon after the Snord, still bleary eyed, trotted into the chamber.

"Yes, Great One?"

"Take the prisoner to the west wing and find her a room."

The Snord looked uncertain, as though he were not quite sure if this was some sort of black joke.

"To the west wing," N'Borg reiterated. "Make sure she is guarded until I send further instructions."

"Thank you, Great One," Leila said, executing a curtsy which N'Borg found extremely gratifying. "You are most gracious."

"And fetch her a clean robe," N'Borg added, before he could stop himself.

"As you command," replied the Snord, standing to one side as Leila brushed past him and out into the corridor.

The Snord was still wondering if his ears had been playing tricks when, out of earshot of N'Borg's chamber, Leila stopped and turned to face her guard.

"If you ever push me in the back again, or ever put so much as a smelly trotter on me, I shall see to it that the Great One has you flogged," Leila threatened venomously.

"I ask your pardon," snuffled the Snord, averting his eyes.

"Granted," replied Leila graciously. "And when you fetch my robe, I also want you to find a good-sized tub and plenty of hot water."

"No! Please!" whimpered the Snord, wide eyed with fear. "Do not boil me! I shall serve you well."

Leila laughed out loud. "I want it to wash myself," she explained.

"Wash? What is wash?" asked the Snord, mystified.

Leila looked at the Snord and laughed again. "I should have known by your smell that you wouldn't understand. Still, I'll soon fix that. If you're going to serve me, you're going to have to change a few of your habits."

"As you wish, my Lady," replied the Snord.

Leila smiled. These Snords were easy to influence. Her guard seemed to have forgotten already that N'Borg had referred to her as 'the prisoner', and she acted as though she possessed considerable authority. Well, perhaps she would. It was not going to be so easy getting N'Borg to co-operate but, given time, she felt sure she could soften him. Yes, it might be bleak and cold here, but already it had its compensations.

N'Borg summoned Leila for 'further questioning' early the next morning. He was troubled. He felt as though he had treated the girl — who, he knew, was nothing more than a common-born settlement dweller with no recognisable power — much too leniently. But he could not resist the temptation to speak with her again. This time he would show her the true face of N'Borg. He would strike fear into her heart and leave her in no doubt that his reputation as an unfeeling, compassionless tyrant was justified.

He was not prepared for the sight of Leila who breezed into his chamber looking far different than she had done the previous night, followed obediently by her "pet" Snord. She executed another respectful curtsy.

"You sent for me, Great One?" She smiled, pleased to note the obvious astonishment in N'Borg's face. She was a maiden transformed. Her hair was clean and combed; her skin clear of dungeon-dirt; and her robe, a deep, luxuriant purple, matched

N'Borg's in shade. Her face was radiant with well-being, and an aura of fragrance which vanished as quickly as it was caught and tantalised the senses, seemed to rise from her like a morning flower.

"What is the meaning of this?" demanded N'Borg, ignoring Leila and addressing the Snord.

"My Lord?"

"This girl," replied N'Borg accusingly. "You bring her before me like a queen, not a prisoner. Explain yourself!"

"My Lord, it was as she commanded," stammered the Snord, obviously confused.

"*She* commanded?" N'Borg thundered. "Who is *she* to command anything?" He gave Leila a sideways glance. She was certainly clever. "And you," said N'Borg, stepping forward and jabbing the Snord in the chest with the point of a sharp fingernail. "What has happened to you? You smell almost pleasant!"

"I have washed," replied the Snord. "The mistress ... err ... prisoner commanded it. She said I was ... umm ... an insult to her nose."

"Did she now," N'Borg hissed, his voice heavy with sarcasm. "I will talk to you later. Now leave. You offend my sight rather more than my nose."

"Yes Lord." The Snord bowed, first to N'Borg, and then, automatically to Leila, before leaving the chamber thoroughly confused.

"So," began N'Borg, turning his back to Leila so she could not distract him, "you claim to have no power yet turn your guard into a servant. Then you come before me dressed like a queen, not a prisoner."

Leila made no reply but began to sob, quietly. When he turned, N'Borg found her looking down at the floor, tears dripping, one by one, from the end of her nose onto the stone floor.

"Stop that nonsense now!" N'Borg ordered. "I shall be deceived by your guile and trickery no longer!"

"Oh, you're so unfair," she protested, sobbing yet more loudly. "I felt so ashamed and unworthy when I was first brought before you. So I thought I should repay your kindness by making myself more presentable and not such an insult to your eyes." She sniffled dramatically, and wiped her nose on a small handkerchief.

"I am not kind!" N'Borg snapped. "Never, never can I be accused of kindness!"

"You are! You are! You have treated me with such courtesy and understanding," Leila replied, before adding in a small voice, "Until now."

"You do not seem to understand," N'Borg said, growing ever more exasperated, "that you are a prisoner."

"Why?"

"Because you belong to the lands under the power of The Council of Wizards."

"I belong nowhere," mumbled Leila, "except between worlds. Like you, I am alone."

"Alone? Me? I am surrounded by servants."

"That's different, and well you know it," Leila replied, almost chiding. "You have no friends."

"How many times must I tell you? Happiness, kindness and friendship are of no use to me. They only make me weaker."

"Everyone needs at least one friend," said Leila.

"I don't," N'Borg replied emphatically.

"So what shall become of me?"

"I haven't decided yet," N'Borg admitted, "but you must stop acting like a guest. It creates a bad impression."

"So I am still a prisoner even though I have not the slightest intention of attempting to escape?"

"Your behaviour does not become a prisoner," N'Borg repeated lamely.

"Whatever you desire, Great One," Leila conceded. "I shall change back into my own clothes and return to the dungeons."

"That will not be necessary," replied N'Borg, his tone softening slightly. "It would only attract more attention."

"So how do I please the Great One?" Leila asked, her request carrying the faintest hint of impatience.

"You can stop trying to convince yourself that I am something other than what you see. Beware, Leila," N'Borg said in a low voice, wondering at the strange feeling saying the girl's name had provoked in him, "nothing can change me, and I will destroy anything which attempts to do so. That includes you. I shall never permit my power to be compromised."

Leila said she understood but, in reality, thought no such thing. N'Borg was only trying to maintain his aloofness for the sake of his public image. Given time, she would transform him and his dismal stronghold. Already, she had begun to daydream again. She was still the Queen Between Worlds, but the King now began to resemble N'Borg. She had to admit that he was not as handsome as her original vision, but he had such power. At the moment, his power was solely destructive, but Leila would help to redirect it. N'Borg would be kind, so kind that everyone would come to love him and his fierce looks became of no consequence. The Krak would be festooned with flowers and filled with the sound of sweet music, dance and laughter. Then the sun would shine here and Leila would be happy; so very happy.

It seemed N'Borg's chosen course of action over the period when Harvest was all but spent and the days grew colder as the Season Cycle began to turn to winter, was to pretend Leila no longer existed. She knew he often asked questions of the Snords detailed to watch over her, but he declined to approach, or summon her again to his chamber. Whilst this set back Leila's plans for breaking down N'Borg's coldness towards her, the edge of her resolve was whetted rather than blunted by his reticence.

She began to make small changes. The mosses and lichens, which were one of the few signs of plant life in and around the Krak, were taken and transplanted by Leila in the gaps between the stones along her corridor. Here and there she made and set out small tapestries, or collages fashioned from scraps of colourful material, upon the stone floors. All small touches which, though N'Borg noted, he thought likely to cause an unnecessary disturbance if he ordered their removal. Little by little, Leila began to alter the atmosphere of the west wing. The torches lighting the corridor were frequently sprinkled with incense looted by the Snords from settlements they had attacked previously, and it did much to drive away the damp, musty smell of coldness and decay which pervaded the rest of the Krak. Always, a small fire was kept burning brightly in her room, fuelled by scraps and oddments brought for Leila by the Snords. They had begun to volunteer for duty on the west wing. It was noticably warmer than their draughty, overcrowded barracks near the maiden's room and, if they were lucky, she would give them hot cakes baked upon the stones of her hearth. Of course, they would still have much preferred to eat Leila herself, but compared to the rations they received, her small treats were very welcome and did much to ensure the Snords went out of their way to remain on good terms with her.

Soon, Leila was able to extend her fantasy a little into her real life by addressing the Snords as though they were her personal servants and the corridors of the west wing her private domain. The fact that Leila had no real authority over the Snords did not appear to bother them in the slightest and they played out their part in her make-believe drama with complete conviction, bowing when she walked past, opening her door for her, and fetching and carrying anything she requested which would not land them in the boiling pot if they were discovered by a Honji. In return, she was as generous as circumstances allowed, always even tempered, responded to their minor transgressions of her rules — such as forgetting to wipe their trotters before entering her room — in a way that made being told off almost a pleasurable experience and, best of all, she was forever singing. Often a whole platoon of Snords would huddle outside Leila's door listening enraptured as her soft, lilting voice carried the words and melody of some song. Their own discordant efforts in the privacy of the corridor at night made them realise just how great a gift a good singing voice can be, and served to increase the esteem in which she was held.

And so it might have always been had N'Chakk's return, just before winter descended, not forced N'Borg into action.

When N'Chakk heard that the girl he had taken captive whilst surveying Plumstock was still alive, he found it difficult to contain his surprise. She must either have some remarkable power N'Borg believed would be of use to him, or she had succeeded in making the Dark Lord behave in a most uncustomary fashion. He could not recollect sensing any power when she had been taken. On the contrary, she had appeared uncommonly naive and innocent. It must be the latter. If this was the case then N'Chakk would do well to get to the bottom of it as soon as possible, for it offered the possibility of him discovering some hitherto unnoticed weakness in N'Borg's defences.

"I am glad to see you well," said N'Chakk, walking straight into Leila's room without knocking. "I must say," he added, "life in the Krak appears to suit you. Your beauty appears to have flourished here."

"I am well," replied Leila, feeling the short hairs on the nape of her neck beginning to rise.

"You have made yourself comfortable," N'Chakk observed, warming his hands over the fire. "The Great One must think highly of you to allow such privileges."

"He has been gracious," said Leila, intuitively recognising that N'Chakk was probing.

"I am sure," said N'Chakk, a tight-lipped smile breaking across his face. "And I am pleased that winter will now give me the time off from my duties to get to know you better. Perhaps you would care to take supper with me this evening?"

"I cannot. I am yet the Great One's prisoner."

N'Chakk smiled again. Leila could almost imagine his tongue flicking out and catching a passing fly.

"Oh, I am sure we need not bother about such things. Trust yourself to my care."

"You have requested permission? I should not like to offend him."

The smile vanished. N'Chakk was irritated by the suggestion that he was as much under N'Borg's control as Leila herself — even if it were true.

"I need no permission," N'Chakk replied acidly. "I will send for you later, when I am ready. Do not delay or you may find out just how powerful I am."

He left his threat hanging in the air, marching out of Leila's room without bothering to close the door behind him.

"I hear you have been talking to the prisoner," N'Borg began, trying to sound matter-of-fact.

"Prisoner, my Lord?"

"The girl you sent from Plumstock."

"Oh, the girl. I see . . ." breathed N'Chakk. "I took her presence in the west wing to mean . . ."

"Never mind what you thought," N'Borg interrupted, banging the base of his staff on the floor. "For what reason did you speak with her?"

"I apologise if I have in any way offended you, Great One," N'Chakk replied, his voice like syrup, "but I believed all prisoners were mine to interrogate as I wished."

N'Borg regarded N'Chakk coldly. "Remarkable how you now choose to call her a prisoner," he growled, his voice heavy with suspicion. "Well, speak! What did you discover?"

"Very little, my Lord. She is clever and does not give of information freely."

"Strange," said N'Borg, almost smiling, "I have found her most co-operative."

"I'm certain. She is ... how shall I say ... a very pleasing companion."

"She is a settlement dweller, nothing more," N'Borg replied, his brow furrowing.

"Quite. But so very charming. I have rarely seen such . . ."

"Enough!" N'Borg bellowed. "Unless you have some good

reason beyond ascertaining her value as a guest, I do not want you . . . I *forbid* you to speak with her again."

"Forbid, Lord? . . ."

"Yes." N'Borg caught sight of the half-sneer he so detested cross N'Chakk's face. "She is, as you have noticed, very clever and full of deceit and guile. I have not yet decided what is to be done with her," he added, by way of an explanation.

"As you command," N'Chakk agreed. He bowed and walked out of N'Borg's chamber still smiling. If he was not mistaken, the Dark Lord was jealous.

That same night, whilst all except the night-watch slept, N'Borg walked over to the west wing. News of his coming travelled before him like ripples across the surface of a lake and, as the Great One passed by, the Snords on duty were already standing to attention. They knew he must be preoccupied. It was rare indeed for N'Borg to pass along a corridor or across a courtyard without stopping to tell at least one Snord they were overdue for a flogging for not polishing their tusks. (I've often thought it odd that N'Borg prefers to keep the Snords in a state of dishevellment and squalor, and yet is reputed to be almost fanatical about tusk-cleaning.)

As N'Borg approached Leila's room he could not help but notice the change in atmosphere. Evidence of her handiwork was everywhere and the air was markedly warmer and scented delicately. It felt as though winter, which raged across the Waste of Shugg, had not dared come here. Outside, the wind howled and drove the snow into deep drifts against the black walls. Here, it might almost be Reawakening.

Outside her door, two Snords were standing to attention, hardly able to disguise their nervousness as he approached.

"Go back to your barracks," he ordered. "Do not return here again this night."

The Snords bowed and shuffled away down the corridor, reluctantly. They had promised their Honji officer two days' rations if he gave them guard duty outside the maiden's door.

There was fierce competition these days for a detail serving on the west wing.

Once certain the Snords had gone and he was alone, N'Borg produced a small krystal and, raising it high on the palm of his hand, incanted a spell with such deliberation his voice rose little above a whisper. Every torch in the corridor was snuffed out in a single breath, like a child blowing out the candles on their Birth-thisday cake. The krystal suddenly pulsed with blue light that crackled through the quiet air of the corridor as though it were a bolt of lightning, transforming the tight-fitting stones of the walls into squares of silver and black, before subsiding to a steady glow which threw a mantle of blue light about N'Borg's head and shoulders.

Silently, he opened the door and stepped inside. The girl was sleeping, now bound in the powerful chains of his incantation. Like a wraith he glided to her bedside and gently placed the magical stone in the middle of her forehead, speaking soft words, but words which unleashed tremendous power. He would unlock the secrets of her innermost mind and make them visible.

N'Borg could wait no longer. He had to know what Leila thought even though he had a sneaking feeling that, in some sense, he was cheating, using his great power to discover what she might have given freely. Still, he had always viewed cheating as perfectly acceptable if it got what he wanted, and he badly wanted to read Leila's mind. It was for his own protection. No matter how innocent the girl seemed, she might harbour some secret desire to overthrow him. Why else had she spoken with N'Chakk? Yes, had it not been N'Chakk who had sent her to the Krak? She was a spy, working in league with that deceitful schemer! Well, now he would discover their plot. The girl must have believed him a fool to be taken in so easily!

A vision of the Krak, dark and intimidating, materialised slowly in the air between Leila's sleeping form and the high ceiling of her room. For some time, nothing further happened, then, close to where the Krak rose up from the black rock of

Shugg, flowers began to appear. The first, small crimson blooms, seemed to struggle to lift their heads before the lash of the cruel wind, showing in small isolated clumps like specks of blood upon a backcloth of dazzling snow, but as the sun rose higher above the Krak, the wind died away, the snow and ice melted, and a profusion of multicoloured flowers began to spring up, covering the rocks, swelling in the hollows and fissures, and slowly spreading out towards the walls of the Krak itself.

As they touched the walls it seemed they stopped, momentarily recoiling from the coldness. Then, like threads that grew thicker and more robust, tendrils began to creep upwards, grappling for a hold upon the smooth stone until, reaching the crenellated watchtowers and the lip of high walkways, they took firm hold. The tendrils burst into leaf, then into countless white bell-shaped flowers.

With a reluctant groan, as though finally yielding to tremendous pressure, the thick gates of the Krak's main entrance swung open and allowed the crowd of flowers to march in.

N'Borg, watching in wonder as his stronghold succumbed to the invasion of the flowers, suddenly noticed two figures standing upon a small balcony above the gates. He focused his concentration upon them, bringing them closer and closer until, stifling a gasp of amazement, he recognised them. One was Leila: the other, himself.

"Look at me!" Leila enthused, catching hold of his hand and laughing lightly as she did so. "All I have dreamed of has come to pass!"

"You are Queen," N'Borg confirmed, actually smiling.

"Yes! Queen Between Worlds!" Leila radiated happiness as intensely as the sun gave warmth.

A small, dark-haired girl ran out onto the balcony holding a small bunch of flowers. These she gave to N'Borg, and clasped her arms about his knees, completely unafraid.

"Papa, are you coming to play now? You did promise."

"Later," N'Borg laughed, stroking her hair fondly. "I must talk awhile longer with your mother. Go and ask N'Chakk to entertain you."

No sooner was his name mentioned than N'Chakk materialised on the balcony — but a very different figure from the one N'Borg knew. Gone were his dark robes. In their place he wore a suit of vivid red and yellow which culminated in a pointed hood that all but covered his head. Only his nose and beard protruded, comically. Here and there, small bells were stitched to his suit, finished with a single large bell on the points of his curving red shoes and the very tip of his crescent-shaped hood. He looked absolutely ridiculous!

"The Princess wishes you to entertain her," N'Borg instructed, trying not to laugh openly.

"Yes, Great One," N'Chakk replied, bowing so low the bell on the end of his hood jangled upon the stone floor. "What does she wish?"

"Stand on your head! I like that trick the best," she said excitedly.

"Oh no, Your Majesty; anything but that! You know it makes me dizzy."

"Yes! Do it! Do it!" the Princess urged, clapping her hands with glee.

"As you please," N'Chakk conceded.

In a trice he was standing on his hands, the hood of his suit squashed so that the bell rang just underneath his nose. N'Borg, Leila and the Princess roared with laughter.

Watching the vision unfold before him, N'Borg felt an uncustomary smile begin to creep across his face, and a strange lightness of being, as though a heavy weight which rested upon his heart was being slowly lifted. In the same instant, somewhere in the back of his mind, a warning voice spoke out.

"Beware! This is false. A mere trick to rob you of your power and turn you into a fool. Resist this temptation, it will destroy you! Fight! Fight!"

N'Borg's smile evaporated. The weight began to descend. He forced the flowers back and concentrated hard until the creepers relinquished their hold and fell, withered to dust, from the walls. The sun was diminished. The wind began to gather strength.

Perhaps that was sufficient, he thought, not at all certain he wanted to destroy the scene any further.

"More! More! Fight! Fight! It is an illusion!"

N'Chakk and the Princess vanished in twin clouds of vapour. Now, as the flowers continued to recede, N'Borg faced Leila, her eyes beginning to fill with tears. Once more the Krak dominated a barren landscape. The wind turned cold, whipping spitefully across the balcony.

"This is what I am, and all I can ever be," N'Borg said.

"No! You have seen there is more!" Leila cried.

"This is all," N'Borg repeated. "Is it enough?"

Leila turned slightly before answering. "If this is all that you will give me then it is what I must accept."

"You shall be Queen?"

"Yes, said Leila softly. "I am destined to be Queen Between Worlds, whatever the shape of the realms which lie to either side. Earth or air, fire or water, good or evil, I shall rule between them."

The vision faded, leaving N'Borg standing in the silence at Leila's bedside. In the wash of fading light from the dying krystal he noticed her cheek was wet with tears.

"Tomorrow you shall be Queen," he whispered, lifting the Krystal gently from her forehead.

Leila turned, murmured something incomprehensible, and slept on.

Leila was awoken when a Snord clattered into her room bearing a small wooden tray. "Breakfast my Lady," he said respectfully, setting the tray down rather ungracefully on a small table at her bedside.

"How dare you awaken me you foul-smelling wretch!" Leila snapped.

The Snord looked as though he had been stung. "It is I, Bellom, your faithful servant. Have I not always brought you breakfast when I could?"

Leila was, herself, surprised by her manner and tone. Her voice was as harsh as her reaction had been out of character. "Sorry Bellom," she said, sinking back upon her pillows. "You are kind. I think I must be unwell."

"The Great One sends word," the Snord said, comforted by Leila's apology. "He will see you in his chamber as soon as you are dressed."

"Yes, I thought he might," Leila said, immediately wondering why she thought any such thing. N'Borg had not spoken to her directly since she had appeared before him in her new robe.

She looked over at Bellom, who was clumsily attempting to smooth the creases from the robe with his large trotters.

"Don't touch that you oaf!" Leila shrieked, "I don't want your stench on me!" Bellom recoiled as though the dress, not Leila, had berated him. "Get out!" she hissed. "Get out before I have you boiled!"

Bellom departed hurriedly. Even his small mind knew something was badly wrong with Leila. Never had she spoken so shrewishly. And her face seemed drained of its colour. Perhaps she was sickening? Settlement dwellers never lasted long in the Krak. If the torture chamber didn't finish them, the climate did.

Leila entered N'Borg's chamber with an air of such complete assurance it made N'Chakk — who was skulking just inside the door — stiffen in surprise. N'Borg was sure to be outraged by her manner.

"What are you gaping at?" she spat.

N'Chakk's eyebrows shot up so high they seemed to vanish beneath his hairline. "You . . . you dare to speak to me . . ."

"Keep your horrid tongue in your mouth or I'll have it cut out," Leila threatened, before N'Chakk could think of a reply to her first insult. She turned her back upon him and dropped N'Borg a deep curtsy. "How may I serve you, Great One?"

"I think you know the answer already," N'Borg replied,

relishing N'Chakk's obvious discomfort.

"I am to be your queen?"

"If you agree to my terms."

N'Chakk's jaw had dropped so much his beard might have brushed the floor. Was this some game? A joke at his expense?

Leila suddenly held her hands to her head, swaying slightly as though she might faint. "I do not feel . . . I cannot think . . . What is happening to me? . . ."

"The confusion will soon pass," N'Borg said calmly. "Do not try to resist any longer, it will only cause you pain."

N'Chakk's eyes flashed. So, that was it! The girl was placed under a powerful enchantment!

"You agree?" N'Borg asked again.

"I do. I shall be yours to command until . . ."

"That is sufficient," N'Borg concluded, before Leila could finish. "N'Chakk, you will see to it that everyone knows I have taken a queen. N'Leila is to be obeyed in all things and is answerable to me, and me alone."

"Yes, My Lord," N'Chakk stammered, bowing low and starting for the door.

"I think you have forgotten something," N'Borg added, halting N'Chakk in mid-stride.

"My Lord?"

"Show Queen N'Leila your fealty."

For a moment it looked as though N'Chakk might refuse but, catching the flash of warning in N'Borg's eye, he bowed stiffly. "My Queen," he murmured, almost choking on the words.

N'Chakk almost ran out of the chamber, the tips of his ears reddening with rage. Once again N'Borg had outwitted him. Now, to add insult to insult he was to kneel to a common settlement girl! Sometimes, N'Chakk felt certain that fate was forever singling him out to be the one who received the stale slice of cake!

That evening, when the stars shone clear and cold, N'Borg and Leila appeared upon the balcony overlooking the main gate. Below, standing to attention, shivering in the wind, every single occupant of the Krak stood upon the rocks of Shugg to witness the betrothal. N'Chakk, still seething with rage and hatred, performed a terse, joyless ceremony, set down by N'Borg himself. Once complete, the black legions of N'Borg knelt to forswear their allegiance to their new queen, N'Leila.

One Snord, far enough away from the balcony to escape notice, looked sideways, his eye caught by a small circle of flowers which struggled to hold their heads above the snow. He wondered if they might be good to eat. Slowly, he reached out towards the crimson blooms, the like of which he had never seen before. As he touched the first delicate stalk, the wind, as though it had sensed his intention, cut low across the ground and scythed through the flowers, scattering petals across the snow like tears of blood.

So N'Leila became a Queen Between Worlds. She stood between the brute ignorance of the black legions of Snords and Honji who knew no better and the corrupt manipulations of N'Borg and N'Chakk who worshipped evil for the power it gave them over others. And in her own mind she knew two voices. The first, and strongest, believed and revered her master, N'Borg's, every word and deed. But a smaller, weaker voice existed within which, from time to time, spoke in kindness and compassion, holding her back at the very edge of the black abyss from which hearts can never return once fallen.

The attack on Plumstock, which followed at the end of the Season of Reawakening after her coronation, reflected her influence. Though the attack was unprovoked and merciless, with all the menfolk put to the sword or enslaved, the womenfolk were spared and, after being herded together, were made to listen to an official message by Queen N'Leila herself. She urged them to see the attack as a liberation, and opportunity to break the shackles of domesticity to which they had given themselves and go in search of true happiness and fulfillment. For most, her words were an insult. She had allowed the destruction of all the happiness they had ever desired or wanted. But there were others who, though few in number, heeded her advice and left Plumstock to pursue their own, private dreams.

verlooking the Waste of Shugg, N'Leila is betrothed to N'Borg.

FAR FROM HOME

Adraught of cold air disturbed the parchments littering the table in front of Turfen, sending two or three sheets fluttering to the floor of the Council Chamber. He rose from his chair, sighing. He had been trying all morning to write up the minutes of the last Council meeting but there had been one disturbance after another.

First Ruegan had been in to request he be excused from attending the meeting arranged for after dinner. He was 'up to his eyebrows' with work and desperately needed complete the test run of some prototype while there was no wind. What this prototype was exactly, only Rueggan knew, and he was loath to give Turfen — or anyone else for that matter — more than a vague reply. Not that Turfen minded: where Rueggan was concerned it was sometimes safer not to get too involved or ask questions. But he had been a little annoyed that the Inventor-Wizard had chosen to ignore all his previous warnings not to bring any Gorphs into the Obelisk. No sooner had they begun talking than two of the little creatures had scuttled out from beneath Rueggan's cape and begun to fight over possession of some trinket. For all Turfen's shouting, the two Gorphs had continued with their argument and finally knocked a full inkwell over three sheets of his best handwriting. Rueggan and the Gorphs had made a discreet withdrawal, leaving Turfen to mop up the mess himself.

He had only just seated himself to begin his task anew when Hottlepottle, the temperamental Obelisk chef, had burst through the door, his face so red and distorted with anger that his eyes appeared to be in danger of popping from their sockets in order to relieve the build-up of pressure behind them.

"I'll cut off his ears and fricasee them!" he bellowed, waving an evil-looking knife dangerously close to Turfen's beard. "Have you seen that excuse of an apprentice hereabouts?"

"Who?"

"Why, Zygmund, of course. When I catch up with him there won't be enough of him left to fill a pudding bowl!"

Turfen was familiar enough with Hotpot's explosive personality to guess that Zygmund's crime was likely to be of a very minor nature. Still, it was wise to show some sympathy.

"What's he done this time?" Turfen enquired, shuffling his parchments in the hope that Hotpot would take the hint and make his complaint as brief as possible.

Hotpot inhaled deeply, as though building up his internal pressure to its absolute maximum. "The little insect put pebbles in my sponge cake mixture instead of diced fruit!"

"Really,? That's not like Zygmund. Are you sure it's him that's responsible?"

"Who else could it be?" Hotpot thundered. "I turn my back on him and the next moment there's my wonderful sponge mix full of old pebbles! I'm going to put him through my root grater when I find him!"

"Well, I've not seen him," concluded Turfen. "Now, if there's nothing else, I would like to get on with my work."

Hotpot brandished his knife again in frustration before storming out of the Council Chamber like a Mahoudha with its tail on fire, still cursing vehemently and slamming the door so hard that Turfen would not have been at all surprised if the noise was heard in Keldorran.

"You'll never guess what I've done," said Haapf, poking his head around the edge of the door as soon as Turfen had turned his attention back to his work.

"Put pebbles in Hotpot's sponge mix, if I'm not mistaken." Turfen sighed.

Haapf's smile evaporated. "How d'you know?" he asked, obviously disappointed.

"Oh, when one has lived in The Obelisk as long as I have, one gets a kind of sixth sense," Turfen replied, without looking up from the parchment before him.

"Amazing," said Haapf, impressed.

"Yes, it's something I've developed over the course of many

seasons. Why, I could tell you what's likely to happen between now and dinner if I wanted."

"Never!" Haapf replied.

"Suit yourself," Turfen said, quietly. "It makes no difference to me if you believe it or not."

"Go on, then," Haapf challenged. "Prove it!"

"Well, I predict that sometime before dinner is served, Zygmund will manage to persuade Hotpot that he was not responsible for the pebbles in the sponge mix. Shortly after this, Hotpot will then begin to search his mind for other likely culprits. Out of a short list of, say, ten, the name of a certain wizard, well known for his practical jokes, will almost certainly occupy the first nine places — the tenth being the remote possibility that a wandering Trolle mistakenly took Hotpot's mixing bowl for a bucket of quick drying building wattle and generously added a shovelful of pebbles. When the dinner gong sounds and all the hungry occupants of The Obelisk arrive in the refectory, Hotpot will be waiting to give a special welcome to his chief suspect . . . " Turfen looked up, gave a brief smile, then continued with his work.

"Unfortunately, I don't think I shall be able to attend dinner today," said Haapf, "there are certain spells I simply must write down in the privacy of my own dormitory."

"Behind locked doors, I suppose?" Turfen replied.

"Quite," said Haapf. "So if you'll give Hotpot my apologies and tell him I've gone to Sobul for the rest of the season, I would be most grateful."

Haapf vanished, leaving Turfen smiling to himself and, once more, at peace.

But now the source of the draught which had blown Turfen's parchments off the table revealed itself. Shepf, robes a-flapping, swept into the Council Chamber," attended by quite a stiff breeze.

"Do you mind turning that off," Turfen requested, struggling to hold the rest of his parchments in place.

"What?" asked Shepf, mystified.

"That breeze of yours," replied Turfen, exasperation beginning to surface in his voice. "I'd be grateful if you could remember to leave your work at home in the future."

"Awfully sorry," Shepf apologized, and, with a nonchalant wave, dismissed the breeze, sending it out through a window. (I've often wondered what becomes of all the magical winds Shepf discards. Perhaps they join together and go howling over The Kappah or The Waste of Shugg?) "I haven't been able to concentrate since I saw that dastardly dragon this morning," he continued. "I can't help but feel uneasy in my bones when he's about."

"Dragon? What dragon?"

"N'Grall, of course. Don't tell me no one else reported seeing him?"

"Not to my knowledge," Turfen replied, forgetting all about his work for the moment. "I'm sure if anyone from the Obelisk had spotted him I'd have been informed immediately."

"Well, I'm reporting it now," Shepf said, settling himself in a chair and facing Turfen across the table. "You can be sure something's afoot."

"Where and when did you see him?" Turfen asked, tugging at the end of his beard — a habit that always signalled he was feeling agitated or nervous.

"First thing," replied Shepf. "I got up early to perform a spot of wind-summoning for the birds that I'd been putting off for days when he flew straight over my tower, as bold as you please."

"Did you say anything to him?"

"Like what? Bid him good morning? Of course not. As I told you, he was flying: and in a rush too if you ask me. I don't think he even noticed me."

"In what direction?"

"South-west, at top speed."

Turfen looked thoughtful. "I wonder why . . . It's unusual for any dragon to fly before the sun's warmed things up a bit unless they have to."

"Yes, but he's no ordinary dragon," Shepf reminded. "If he

can stand the cold in The Waste of Shugg, an early morning's not going to bother him in the slightest. Don't forget, he's got that Krystal N'Borg gave him to keep off the cold."

"True," Turfen agreed, "but that still doesn't answer the most important questions. Where was he going and for what reason?"

"Well, you're as wise on that score as I am," admitted Shepf. "Perhaps it was for no reason other than to let us know he's still about."

"If that were true he would have gone out of his way to be seen. Besides, I don't believe N'Borg could possibly think we've forgotten about him with things as they are in Keldorran. The Mugrahs and the Wood-Sprites have been far too busy for that, not to mention the attacks on the outlying settlements and the sighting of Snord patrols all over the place. So, there's some reason behind it, you can be sure of that."

"What then?"

Turfen shrugged and tugged his beard still harder. "Wish I knew," he said, before asking, "What direction did you say?"

"South-west, as near I recall."

"Hmm . . . " Turfen stopped tugging at his beard and studies his shoes, deep in thought. "Only two possibilities suggest themselves to me at the moment," he said, at length. "Either Sobul or the Shadi-Sampi."

"Still doesn't tell us why, even if you are right," Shepf pointed out.

"No, but it's a start," Turfen replied. "Tell Graffyn to ask Grunch if he'll send a dragon to Sobul to see if N'Grall's put in an appearance there."

"And the Shadi-Sampi?"

"More difficult, I'm afraid. It's far too dense for dragon to land there and, even if it could, the Hydro-Glyphs aren't too fond of showing themselves to anyone. Hardly anyone outside the Gadazorri have seen them, and even they are only allowed to when it suits the Glyphs."

"But if, as you say, it's impossible for a dragon to land, there would'nt be much point in N'Grall going in the first place,"

Shepf observed.

"Granted," said Turfen. "So all the more reason for us to check. N'Borg, as you well know, isn't the sort to ever do what we expect. I think I'll try and get a message to Tulan and the Gadazorri and ask them, if they can spare the time, to send a party to have a look. I'd feel a lot easier."

"You never know," said Shepf, trying to sound more optimistic, "it may be nothing."

"Perhaps," Turfen replied, "but, as you say, knowing N'Grall's about makes me feel uneasy in my bones." Turfen went back to his work, still tugging on his beard.

Four days later, a dependable dragon, named Skittle-grampling The Third, (whom everyone, except his parents, called Skit for short), returned tired and dusty-winged from Sobul. Apart from informing Turfen that the trade value of Sobul-cultured Seapod Globes had reached an all-time high on the open market, there was little else worth reporting. The settlement's Fugleman had made the usual 'we think The Council of Wizards are doing a wonderful job!' kind of statement, (which, though polite, is of no real use to anyone except the person saying it) but had not seen anything remotely resembling a dragon of any kind, let alone one which possessed a penchant for unprovoked violence and maliciousness. He would, however, make a public announcement urging all Sobulians to be extra vigilant and report anything suspicious immediately, just to be on the safe side. (And also because there was nothing he liked better than making public announcements!)

"Well that's one possibility we can rule out," said Turfen, after giving a brief account of Skit's report to the rest of the Council. "I don't think we can do anything more for now than wait and see what the Gadazorri say."

"Presuming they say anything," said Graffyn. "We don't even know if they've received the message yet, do we?"

"No, but I had intended to ask you if you'd have another word with Grunch to see if he might spare a dragon or two for a spot of coastal reconaissance," replied Turfen. "The sooner we find them the better I'll feel."

"I should like to request a favour of this honourable assembly if I may," said Rueggan.

"Speak, my friend," bade Turfen,

"I had been planning to visit the Gadazorri myself next Reawakening to show them my latest design alterations to The Long Ship and invite their expert comment. However, if we are going to send a dragon to locate them, might it not be possible for me to charter the flight as a paying passenger? That way I would have the opportunity of conveying our message, assessing the situation for myself, and showing them my plans. I could then spend my time over winter on further development without having to wait."

"Who's going to pay?" asked Graffyn, his mind, as always, turning to thoughts of a business nature. "Grunch will charge top rates for such a short notice booking."

"I should be willing to meet the differences in costs myself," Rueggan replied, earnestly.

"I don't think that will be necessary," Turfen interjected. "Grunch may drive a hard bargain when it comes to business on a day to day basis, but he's always been more than co-operative where the Great Design is concerned. I'm sure Graffyn will be able to negotiate a substantial discount."

"I wouldn't bet on it!" Graffyn mumbled, into his beard.

"Rueggan's just trying to fix a discount holiday package for himself, if you ask me!" accused Haapf, before disintegrating into fits of giggles.

"Please try and treat this seriously," Turfen chided. "The future security of us all may depend on the decisions we make here today."

"Hear! Hear!" Shepf agreed. "Besides, those who have gained something of a reputation for frivolity and questionable use of Council funds should not be so quick to make accusations." He shot Happf a reproachful look.

"I can't think what you mean!" retorted Haapf, looking

wounded.

"Who was it who wasted two days of Council resources when he turned the shovels and pickaxes of an entire Trolle working party into bunches of flowers?" Shepf reminded.

"They looked much more colourful," Haapf replied, defensively. "It was only a joke, after all."

"A very expensive one," said Shepf, trying to suppress a smile. (It was true, the Trolles, all waving gigantic bunches of brightly coloured flowers, had looked like a huge, animated flower border!)

"I think we should return to the issues facing us now," Turfen intervened. "And I think Rueggan's request is an excellent idea. Agreed?"

"Agreed!" chorused The Council, unanimously,

"Good!" Turfen concluded. "I shall send news of arrangements to you, Rueggan, as soon as Graffyn has spoken with Grunch. Now, unless there is any other business, I shall bring this assembly to a close . . . " Turfen paused and looked about the chamber, questioningly.

"What about the minutes of the last two meetings?" objected Haapf. "We haven't heard them yet."

"Err . . . I think, in view of circumstances, that it might be better if we left them until some less important occasion," Turfen replied, hurriedly covering the sheets of empty parchments before him with his arm. Sometimes, being The Doyen of The Council of Wizards had its drawbacks . . .

Rueggan was lucky. He had scarcely unpacked his few essential belongings and taken refreshment in the humble, but comfortable room which had been set aside for him, when the Fugleman of Sobul knocked upon the door and informed the wizard he had received word the Gadazorri were due to arrive within the next few days. The local Weather-Watcher was predicting sunshine and fresh North-easterlies, so it was unlikely that there should be any reason for delay.

This was a wonderful start: Rueggan had given The Obelisk plenty of assurances that he would find the Gadazorri but, in truth, had scant idea of how to go about it. Apart from some knowledge of aquadynamics, he knew precious little about the sea. Now he could stop worrying, wait for the Gadazorri to arrive, and do a little sightseeing in the meantime. He could not help but allow himself a wry smile. It looked a though Haapf had been right. He might get a holiday — albeit a brief one — after all!

Much of the old settlement of Sobul had been destroyed by a mudslide caused by freak weather conditions which N'Borg had instigated as a softening blow prior to his attack on The Obelisk in the First Battle. The new buildings, which had been built to replace those lost, reflected the advances made by the Great Design, and Rueggan was pleased to discover that many of the public buildings —such as the covered fish market, the smoke-houses and the assembly hall — had installed plumbing systems originally designed and tested by him. The inventor-wizard soon sought out the workshop of the local architect and spent every day before the arrival of the Gadazorri helping to modify and improve the plans for proposed buildings. This was his idea of relaxation and, though the architect of Sobul thought some of his ideas a little grandiose, Rueggan made many sensible and practical suggestions which could be incorporated in future developments. As always, Rueggan succeeded in making his influence felt as well as making new friends and, when the first Gadazorri sail was sighted rounding the headland to the south, the architect, half-joking and half-serious, promised Rueggan a consultant's position should he ever decide to retire from the Council.

Tulan knew that something must be afoot to find Rueggan so far away from his workshop in the Valley of Wendlock and, after exchanging greetings, listened in silence as the wizard relayed Turfen's request and the reasons behind it.

"A journey to the Shadi-Sampi would be too far to undertake

in one of the Skeats," Tulan observed, motioning towards the row of small vessels drawn up on the beach. "It would need a Rahpan and full crew." He sat down on the sand and looked thoughtfully out to sea. "I cannot say that I much like the idea of letting a Raphan leave the rest of the fleet," he said. "Our strength lies in our unity: that is the way it has always been. On the other hand, if we all set out now for the Shadi-Sampi we would arrive before the orchid-spices were ready for harvesting by the Hydro-Glyphs, as well as interrupting the trade-cycle. We are the only link, some of the settlements have with main ports such as this one, and they depend upon us for news as well as goods they cannot make for themselves.

"Of course, we are aware of the problems," Rueggan admitted, "and in truth, there may be absolutely no cause for concern, in which case the journey might prove to be a waste of effort."

"But if, as Turfen suspects, N'Borg is up to something ... " Tulan interjected.

Rueggan made no reply but a small nod of agreement.

"Could it not wait until we are due to visit the Shadi-Sampi?" Tulan asked.

"That I do not know," Rueggan replied. "All I do know is that Turfen has sent me to find out and, with or without your assistance, that is what I shall do."

"You're twisting my arm," smiled Tulan. "I'm too used to trading to fall for that old trick."

"It's no trick," Rueggan said, earnestly. "I shall go with or without you."

Tulan laughed aloud. "We would be at the Shadi-Sampi before you were even halfway. The only paths lie upon the surface of the sea and, unless you've got a good boat and an experienced crew under your cape, not to mention a guide, then I doubt you'd make it no matter how determined you were."

"Oh, I don't know, said Rueggan, mysteriously. "I might have an idea."

Tulan laughed again. "I'm sure you have. Ideas are never in short supply when you're around." He got to his feet and dusted the sand from his robe. "Well, I'm overdue for a bit of excitement, I suppose. Get your things packed, wizard. We sail on the morning tide."

"Excellent!" Rueggan enthused. "I knew the Council could depend upon the Gadazorri."

"I have my motives," smiled Tulan. "This voyage will give me plenty of opportunity to find out what this idea of yours is."

"Idea? Which one? I've got enough ideas to last you from now until next Reawakening." Now it was Rueggan's turn to laugh.

Ideas were the last thing on Rueggan's mind when Tulan's Rahpan, its famous sail, bearing the motif of a purple fish, filled with the breeze and began to carry them away from Sobul. At first, the inventor wizard had enjoyed the novel sensation of the deck's pitch and roll, and had stood forward, to one side of the high prow, letting his whiskers get dampened with spray. But soon the exhilaration he felt was replaced by an uneasiness in the pit of his stomach. It was not, as he hoped, a product of his imagination, and grew steadily worse until his face assumed a pallor not too many shades lighter than the green of his own robes.

"What ails you my friend?" asked Tulan, lightly, a knowing look in his eye.

"I don't really know," Rueggan replied, swallowing hard. "I feel absolutely awful."

"Perhaps it is hunger?" Tulan suggested, mischievously. "Would you care for a piece of my cured shellfish? It really has the most excellent flavour." He waved the highly seasoned morsel close under Rueggan's nose. "Here, try some."

"Take it away! Please!" Rueggan begged, the smell causing him to recoil and his stomach to threaten a violent counter-reaction. "The thought of food is enough to make me want to . . . " He swallowed hard again and wilted against a narrow mast, looking perfectly wretched. "I think I'm going to die!" he moaned, forlornly.

"No, my friend, it only feels that way. You have the sickness which often affects land dwellers when they come aboard. It will pass, I promise you."

"When?" asked Rueggan, hoping it would be soon.

"A day, maybe two. Certainly no more than three; although you can never tell . . . "

Rueggan groaned. "I'm going to lie down until I can put my feet back on dry land."

"We should reach Garton at first light, then you can take a quick walk ashore if you like."

"How long before the Shadi-Sampi?"

"You'll be long cured by then," laughed Tulan. "We're going to sail with the rest of the fleet to Garton, Karesh and Poloppo before leaving them and heading direct for the Shadi-Sampi alone. There we'll wait for the others to complete the usual trade-route and join us in time for collecting the orchid-spices."

"I might wait in Garton for your return," Rueggan said, weakly.

"So much for the wizard who, only yesterday, was telling me he would reach the Shadi-Sampi at any cost," Tulan teased. "Now look at you, and we've only just lost sight of Sobul!"

"That's typical of a trinket-trader," Rueggan returned. "Always ready to take advantage when you're down."

Tulan and his first mate, Krellick, both laughed loudly. "That's what I like to see," said Tulan, chuckling, "a bit of fighting spirit!"

"I couldn't fight my way past an angry fly at the moment," Rueggan moaned.

"Go and lie down," replied Tulan. "You never know, you might need all your strength when we reach the Shadi-Sampi."

"I don't care if N'Borg and his entire army are there," Rueggan said, wobbling unsteadily across the deck. "I'd sooner try and fight the whole lot of them with my bare hands than spend a moment longer than I have to on this piece of driftwood."

As Tulan had predicted, Rueggan was fully recovered by the time they waved farewell to the rest of the fleet and set a course to take them directly to the Shadi-Sampi.

"How long do you think it will be before I return to Wendlock?" asked Rueggan, one night whilst Tulan was giving him a lesson in navigating by the stars.

"That depends very much on what, if anything, we discover." answered Tulan. "Given a straightforward trip with no hitches we should make the mouth of the swampland, the Delta, in seven or eight days. The rest of the fleet should catch up with us ten days or so after." Tulan paused and scratched his head, thinking. "I should say we could have you back in Sobul in plenty of time to catch a dragon-ride back to The Obelisk before winter. I must allow time for the fleet to reach safe harbour before the storms begin so that we can work on repairs and be ready for the next Reawakening. Why do you ask? Are you homesick already?"

"Oh, no," said Rueggan, "although I am a bit worried about leaving the Gorphs in the care of others."

"I'm sure they'll be well looked after," consoled Tulan.

"Of that I have no doubt," Rueggan replied. "My concern is not for the Gorphs, but for the poor unfortunate who Turfen sends to keep an eye on them. There's one job he'll have difficulty in finding volunteers for!" Rueggan chuckled quietly, before looking back up at the stars. "They fascinate me," he said, trying to remember the Gadazorri names which Tulan had given to the most important. "Have you ever wondered about them, Tulan?"

"How do you mean?"

"Well, for instance, how far away are they?"

"Pretty far, I should say," Tulan replied. "I know you can't shoot them down with a bow, like I've heard some say."

"It never fails to amaze me what some will believe," agreed Rueggan. "Mind you, I think the truth may sound even more unbelievable."

"Why?"

"Call it wizard's intuition, if you like, but I've got the feeling they are very far away indeed. Much further than you could possibly imagine. If they are, then they would also be extremely large."

"What makes you say that?" asked Tulan, not certain if it really mattered, anyway.

"On a clear day you can see the Mountains of Kappah from the coast, can you not?"

"Yes."

"Now, you know they are huge, but how big do they actually look?"

"Ah, I see your point," said Tulan. "So the stars might be as big as the mountains, just further away."

"Possibly even bigger."

"Very interesting," admitted Tulan, "but I can't see why it should interest you so much."

"That's because you don't think like I do," said Rueggan. In fact, sometimes I believe that nobody else in Krystonia does. Why is it that the real importance of such questions is overlooked? Beginning to answer them could change the whole way we view Krystonia."

"Now you've completely lost me," Tulan confessed. "It's all far too complicated."

"Just the opposite. It's very simple. And it should be of interest to you above all people."

"Why?" asked Tulan, beginning to feel like an infant who understands nothing but is forever asking 'why.'

"Your ancestor, Captain Valdar sailed off the edge of the sea because he did not believe that the sun was swallowed at the end of every day and replaced by a new one the next morning, did he not?"

Tulan nodded.

"Was he right?"

Tulan shrugged. "I cannot decide either way. He did not return with the answer."

"Well, I for one am convinced he was. I'm certain of it."

Rueggan's voice had started to become charged with a strange mixture of excitement and frustration. "You've been staring up at the truth since you were an infant in your mother's arms!" Rueggan pointed at the stars. "Do the same stars appear in the same place night after night?"

"They do change from season to season," consented Tulan.

"Alright, alright," dismissed Rueggan, as though shoo-ing away a persistent fly. "Let me put the question more carefully. If I were to stand upon this deck, at the same time, in the same place, exactly one full season-cycle from now, would not the stars be in the same position?"

"They would."

"So what is the most logical explanation?"

Tulan shrugged again.

"Quite obviously, it is that they are the same stars!"

"So?"

"So they do not get swallowed by the sea and replaced by new ones on the next night, just as it is not a new sun, or new moons that we see. They are the same, the very same, always! Therefore, there is no edge to the sea!"

"How can you say . . . "

"Look!" said Rueggan, almost shouting. He licked the end of finger and traced an imaginary circle on the deck. "The circle is us. The stars merely keep going around it!"

"But you look!" argued Tulan. "Is the sea flat or is it curved?"

"It only looks flat," replied Rueggan. "It's all a matter of scale, like the stars and the mountains."

"Tulan shook his head. "You may be wiser than I," he replied, "but I know what I see with my eyes. The sea is flat." He shook his head again. "A round sea, indeed!" He laughed, signalling the end of the discussion. "I must get some rest, I suggest you do the same."

Tulan walked off to his cabin, leaving Rueggan alone on the deck. "I'm right! I know it!" he whispered, but only the star's were listening.

"The Delta Cap'n!"

At the lookout's call Rueggan rushed over to stand beside Tulan. "We're here, then," he said, obviously pleased that the end of the outward voyage was over after what had seemed to be an interminable number of days.

"We are," confirmed Tulan, then, turning to Krellick he said, "Bring her about and take us back up to that inlet we passed a while since."

"Why are we sailing away from the Delta's mouth?" Rueggan enquired.

"Because I have not forgotten the purpose of our voyage," replied Tulan, seeming preoccupied and a little on edge. "I think we should sail back up the coast a little way and find somewhere to hide. Then we can row in with a Skeat under cover of darkness and have a quick look to decide if it's safe enough to bring the Rahpan closer."

"Good idea," agreed Rueggan, impressed by Tulan's caution. "Stick our whiskers around the door before we enter the room, eh?" he said, quoting an old spellcasting adage.

"Big fish always let little fish try the bait," returned Tulan, with the Gadazorri equivalent.

Some time later, the Gadazorri crew guided the Raphan expertly between the high walls of land which flanked a narrow inlet. The water here was flat, calm, and so clear that, even in the fast-fading light, Rueggan was able to make out schools of fish, flashing silver far below, and trace the rise and fall of the underwater rock formations which thrust upwards from forests of gently waving fronds of weed. Rueggan, who had little experience of the sea, was entranced and hung dangerously over the side of the Rahpan in order to get a clearer view. Tulan who had seen similar sights many times before, was more concerned with concealment. The inlet was ideal from this point of view as well. Only a bird flying directly overhead would have been able to discover the Raphan's berth, so enclosed was the narrow strait of water by the steeply rising ground on all sides.

"I've passed this inlet many times before," Tulan confessed, "but this is the first time I've ever entered it. Strange, how often you discover something new only when you break an established pattern."

"I hope you'll remember that," replied Rueggan. "Particularly when you recall our conversation the other night."

Tulan laughed and shook a finger at the wizard. "And I hope you remember that I said I believed what I saw with my eyes. This inlet I see, therefore I may believe. But stars as big as mountains? . . ."

Just before nightfall, Rueggan, Tulan and four oarsmen descended into the Skeat, leaving charge of the Rahpan in Krellick's capable hands. "If, for any reason, we not return, do not come in for us until the rest of the fleet arrives," Tulan warned. "Your first responsibility is for the safety of the Rahpan."

"Listen at him," retorted Krellick, good naturedly, "Still wet behind the ears and already telling me how to do my job! Get off with you, Son of Tallac."

At Tulan's order, the oarsmen began to pull strongly, their stroke in perfect synchrony. Over the splash of the oars, and the hiss of water parted by the bows of the Skeat as it moved towards the spit, Krellick's voice floated through the gathering gloom. "Safe return Son of Tallac. May the spirits of the seas watch over you."

Once clear of the protection afforded by the high shoulders of land, Rueggan felt the more powerful swell of the open seas as it rolled beneath the small vessel and saw the faces of the oarsmen take on a soft sheen as they warmed to their work.

"Pulling against an incoming tide," observed Tulan, as though reading the wizard's thoughts. "Still, secrecy is more important to us than effort at the moment."

Rueggan nodded his agreement and kept his eyes fixed upon the sparcely-wooded spit of land that jutted out and formed one arm of the Delta where the dark waters flowing from the swamp of Shadi-Sampi were discharged into the sea. He felt his beard begin to bristle. He could almost touch the magic which oozed from the place — a feeling which grew stronger the nearer they drew.

"We'll land on this side," hissed Tulan, "and pull the Skeat up into the trees. Then we'll be able to sneak through and take and look at The Delta."

"Is this place always so creepy?" asked Rueggan, unable to shake off the feeling of disquiet.

"It is," Tulan confirmed. "I've come here every Harvest for longer than I care to remember, and it's never been any different. Mind you," he continued, "this is nothing compared to the swamp itself. In the heart of the Shadi-Sampi, where the Glyphs dwell, you feel as though even the trees are watching."

"Strange that so gentle a race should choose to live in such a place," Rueggan observed.

"Perhaps," agreed Tulan, "but they seem to value privacy more than anything, apart from their music. To be perfectly honest, the Shadi-Sampi is beautiful, but in a disturbing sort of way that I cannot put into words. It's not the place so much as something in the air." Tulan trailed a hand over the gunwale of the Skeat, feeling the water pass through his fingers. "But then, I felt the same when I came with my father to fight at The Obelisk. I don't think that I would ever be happy unless I could smell the sea."

"I feel just the same about my workshop," said Rueggan. "I've missed the smell of wood shavings and parchments. Thinking about it makes me realise how far from home I am. I'm not the sort to give to wandering, I suppose."

"Except in your thoughts," Tulan returned.

"That's different. I don't have any problems with travel arrangements when I want to get back," Rueggan joked.

"Or sickness," countered Tulan, before touching Rueggan's arm, lightly. "I think it better we try to talk as little as possible now," he cautioned. "We're almost there."

The Gadazorri dug their oars deeply and, after giving several powerful, quick strokes, lifted them clear of the water and stowed them in the bottom of the Skeat. Moments later, with the trees on the shore looming large and dark above them, Rueggan felt a slight shudder run along the Skeat's length and the soft grate of the sand against the bows. At Tulan's whispered command, the oarsmen and Rueggan leapt over the side, the sudden shock of the cold water about his knees making the wizard gasp. Together, they ran the small vessel aground, and dragged it up the narrow strip of sand, inside the first row of trees. With only a moment's pause to catch their breath, the six began to steal their way carefully across the spit, led by Tulan, their feet making no sound upon the sandy soil. They had not far to go. At this point, an Om-ba-Don, like Moplos, could have thrown a rock clear over the tapering strip of land. But Moplos, and any other ally for that matter, were far, far away . . .

The Delta appeared dark and quiet — only the occasional splash of a leaping fish breaking the silence. Then, as the party were just about to leave the cover of the trees and walk down to the water's edge, the sound of voices, distant and unclear, reached them. They froze, not sure from which direction the sound had come. They waited, hardly daring to move in case they accidentally snapped off a low branch, or cracked a piece of dead wood.

"C'mon! Faster, you stupid flute-blower!"

The voice was much closer, almost directly beneath them. Rueggan felt Tulan's hand descend to the handle of the cutlass he always wore thrust beneath his waistband.

As though for their benefit, the clouds which had obscured Gos and Ghedra, suddenly broke ranks, illuminating the steeply sloped strand with a wash of light. Two Snords appeared like shadows cut from the surrounding darkness, walking down the shore, a small bundle, glowing faintly, walking half a pace in front.

"That's better," said one, "I can see where I'm bloody going at last!"

"P'rhaps you'll stop complaining now then," replied the other.

"Watch yer mouth, or I'll chuck yer in the water," returned the first, hotly.

"Oh yeah! You an' who's army?"

"Won't taken no army 'cept me t' dump you on yer tail, bonehead!"

"I'd like t' see yer try, fatso!"

"Right! You asked for it! I'm going t' make yer eat . . . "

The Snords' argument was cut short in the same instant that Rueggan noticed two other shadows appear silently behind them. There was a muffled grunt, and both Snords fell face down in the sand. The wizard turned to look at Tulan, but the Gadazorri captain was no longer there. Rueggan was amazed. He had neither heard nor felt Tulan leave his side. Before he had time to comprehend what was going on, the two shadows picked up the bundle that the Snords had been escorting and carried it back into the trees.

"By my beard!" gasped Rueggan, crawling over the where Tulan and the other Gadazorri were hunched over the bundle. "That was quick work!"

Tulan did not respond to Rueggan. Instead he knelt over the prostrate form before him. "Boll! Boll? Is that you?"

The bundle glowed a little more brightly. "Tulan of the Gadazorri? I hear your voice but wonder what brings you here at this time. Are you not early?" it replied, weakly.

"That I am. And well that I am, it seems. What has happened? Why do I find the King of the Hydro-Glyphs taken captive?"

'The King of the Hydro-Glyphs!' thought Rueggan. 'By my beard!'

"They have come to break our music, Tulan. They seek to drive us out or make us serve who they call The Great One. You must help. We are powerless against them!"

"Who? The Snords?"

"No. Myra! Myra?" Boll replied, throwing aside his bonds and getting to his feet.

"Who is Myra?" asked Rueggan.

Boll looked at the ground and replied, quietly, "She was the

Princess Myra: my daughter."

"How came she to turn against you?" asked Tulan.

"That would take too much telling now," Boll replied. "You must come and help us before it is too late. Soon the Shadi-Sampi will belong to the Great One."

"That must not happen. How can we help?" asked Tulan.

"Their magic will not affect your ears as it does ours," replied Boll. "You must drive them away."

"Excuse me," put in Rueggan, "but aren't you overlooking one small matter?" Everyone looked at him, expectantly. "Well, where have the Snords come from? How many of them are here? We may be able to help you against this Myra, but the Snords are a different matter."

"True," agreed Tulan, "We need to sit down and decide upon the best and safest course of action. Boll, you will have to return with us to our Raphan."

"That I cannot," Boll replied, "I would not survive the night outside the Shadi-Sampi. See how dim my light grows even here? I need to return, with or without you, to the swamp as soon as possible. As for the Snords, there are a good number of them, and some bigger, nastier types who tell them what to do."

"Honji," said Rueggan.

"I think they wait to enter the swamp," continued Boll, "but until our magic is completely destroyed they cannot go much further than the end of The Delta. They merely receive captives from Myra's Thane-Glyphs and provide the magical stones which gave them power over us."

"Krystals!" Rueggan said.

"Yes, I believe I have heard them called such," replied Boll. "An extremely large dragon brings them."

"So that's what N'Grall is doing," Rueggan interrupted, again, "Everything's starting to make sense now." He stroked his beard. "But I still don't understand how he manages to land here. I thought there were too many trees."

"The Great One's servants have cut down the trees on the other side of The Delta for him," replied Boll.

"What I don't understand is how the Snords and Honji got here in the first place," said Tulan. "Surely the dragon has not carried them all?"

"No, they arrived first to prepare a way for him," confirmed Boll.

"Then, how? . . . "

"Like Gadazorri," replied Boll. "They come in some kind of vessel which rides upon the water."

Tulan and the other Gadazorri looked shocked. As far as they knew, only they had the knowledge required to build large ships and, for N'Borg's forces to have arrived by sea they would have had to leave from the most westerly edge of The Waste of Shugg and sail right through The Blind Sea — no mean feat of seamanship or navigation given the perpetual storms and thick fog banks from which its name was derived. "How many ships?" asked Tulan, obviously concerned.

"One only. Very large. Much larger than a Raphan. It has left since, no doubt to fetch reinforcements."

"N'Borg's trying to come in by the back door," mused Rueggan, half to himself, before addressing Boll directly again. "Have you seen any other apart from the Snords and the Honji?" he asked, gravely. "In particular, have you seen one similar to me in height, also bearded, and wearing dark robes?"

Boll shook his head. "No. Only those so far described and, occasionally, the dragon. However, we think they await the arrival of someone of importance. They have erected a large shelter and mounted a guard outside. As far as we can tell, there is no resident, but none of the others go near."

"Then we must act quickly," said Rueggan, authoritatively. "If they await N'Chakk, or worse still, N'Borg, and they arrive before we have made our move, all will be lost. My power is no match for either."

"But how shall we get into the swamp?" asked Tulan. "There are no paths and we cannot use the Skeat. They'd see us before we were halfway up the Delta."

"There are paths," Boll corrected. "Alone you would never

find your way but, with me as your guide, it should be possible to reach the swamp if we are cautious."

"Then lead on," bade Rueggan, all for starting out immediately.

"Wait," said Tulan. "I shall return to the Rahpan and tell Krellick what's afoot and pick up a few supplies. I don't want him sailing straight into the Delta, and he must warn the rest of the fleet should they arrive whilst we are gone. Rueggan, you wait with Boll, and keep out of trouble if you can. The rest of us will return as quickly as possible." With that, Tulan, followed by his crew, melted into the darkness, leaving Rueggan, his head full of uneasy thoughts, with the King of the Hydro-Glyphs. His workshop, or the size of the stars, were the last things on his mind now.

The journey into the heart of the Shadi-Sampi was even more taxing than Rueggan and the others had imagined. Where Boll could take to the air and simply fly over the narrow creeks and mud pits which constantly barred their way, they were forced to either wade through or make time-comsuming detours around such obstacles. Frequently, brightly coloured serpents slithered out of the dense vegetation intent on attack but, always, at a sign from Boll, they withdrew, hissing, back into their lairs. Once, as they waded waist deep across the lagoon of stagnating oily water, one of the crew had been seized about the ankles and dragged beneath the surface before anyone could react. Boll had to buzz angrily just above the opaque surface before the Gadazorri, gasping for air, was released. But where Boll seemed to hold sway over most of the swampland creatures, there was nothing he could do to alleviate the depredations of the swarms of winged insects which hovered about the travellers, inflicting painful bites and stings whenever they lighted upon an exposed arm or neck. Often Rueggan had to stop and shake out his beard. In a short space of time he came to understand why the Shadi-Sampi had never been explored by krystal prospectors. If the serpents or the mud pits didn't get you, the insects did!

Natural threats apart, Boll was forever insisting upon complete silence. Myra's Thane-Glyphs knew the byways of the swamp almost as well as he and, even if they were not directly attacked, they could be sure that the Snords and Honji would soon be told that there were intruders in the Shadi-Sampi and to arrange a suitable reception for when they returned.

At last, four uncomfortable days and nights after first setting out upon their journey, Boll — whose skin had grown noticably brighter the deeper they progressed — suddenly called a halt. "We approach The Sacred Ring," he said "I must ask you all to give your word that you will never disclose its location to anyone."

"I don't think I could find it again if I wanted to," Rueggan replied, busily swatting at the insects which had attempted to settle upon his nose as soon as he had stopped walking. "I've been lost for three days at least. I don't think I could even guess in which direction the sea lies."

"Me, too," agreed one of the Gadazorri crewmen. "I won't be in a hurry to repeat that journey again."

"I must have your promise," insisted Boll. "No outsider has ever set foot inside The Ring before."

"You have my word," said Tulan, anxious to get on. The rest of the party nodded in turn.

"Then follow," Boll said. "Take care not to stray off the path. Our magic is strong here. You will be lost forever if you depart from the secret way by so much as a hand's breadth."

'Which doesn't leave much room for mistakes,' thought Rueggan, noticing how tiny and delicate Boll's hands were in comparison to his own.

For a short distance, the path they followed did not appear any different to the other twisting, confounding tracks they had followed in the course of the last few days but, suddenly, Rueggan and the rest of the party found themselves enveloped in a thick, swirling mist. They had not seen it in the distance, or even noticed a gradual thickening; it was as though they had suddenly stepped through some unseen portal and emerged

he secret paths leading to the twilight interior of the Shadi-Sampi swampland are known only
the Hydro-Glyphs.

into a completely different place. The air was cool and fragrant, refreshing after the oppressive, clammy heat of the swamp, and there was a noticable absence of any hungry insect swarms. Hovering a short distance in from of them, Boll, his whole body shining like a lantern of green light, led them onwards, his beating wings describing an orb of luminescence that shimmered brightly about him in marked contrast to the grey, featureless profiles Rueggan and the others had assumed.

The mist became thicker and damper, until Tulan decided that it would be wise for them to join hands. On they went, their robes and beards growing heavy with moisture.

For what seemed an age, the weary travellers followed Boll's light blindly until, from out of the mist, he was joined by others of his kind; obviously overjoyed that the King they had given up for lost had returned safely, and both amazed and curious about the strangers he had brought into their secret realm. They flashed low overhead, stopping briefly to inspect the party before darting away at high speed, trailing ribbons of light in their wake until the mist itself seemed set aglow and Rueggan noticed that his robe had assumed a strange sheen of dull green light. Soon after, they followed the path as it dipped sharply downwards, leading them, (though, then, they knew it not), down into The Sacred Ring of the Hydro-Glyphs.

The melodic sound of water, falling from some height and splashing against rock, was the first change they noticed but, as they descended further, the mist grew thinner until, finally, they appeared on the uppermost lip of a sheer precipice, awash with the same green light − the mist now forming a high ceiling, as though of stormclouds, above their heads.

Down they went, Boll, now walking, leading them to what appeared to be a haphazard jumble of rocks placed in the centre of the floor at the base of the funnel-shaped precipice, from the summit of which a spring erupted and fell in a series of thin waterfalls.

"Impressive," mused Rueggan, to himself. "Very impressive."

As they drew near to the rock pile, another Glyph, a female, almost as tall as Boll himself and with the same regal bearing, came forward to greet them. She touched Boll lightly in the middle of his forhead with the tip of a finger.

"Their customary greeting, I suppose," said Rueggan quietly. "I wouldn't mind giving her a Gadazorri greeting," returned one of the crewmen.

Tulan, overhearing the comment, shot the Gadazorri a warning look. Rueggan could not help but smile. He could understand the crewman's reaction. The female Glyph was stunningly beautiful.

"My Queen," announced Boll, proudly. "Vena."

The party all bowed politely and took it in turns to shake her delicate hand.

"You shall always have our gratitude for bringing our King safe home," she said, sincerely. "The Gadazorri have proved themselves great friends." Then, noticing Rueggan, she added, "And so has? . . . "

"Rueggan Amadeus Bartholong, Son of Timion Bartholong of Kikfarrn," replied Rueggan, thinking it best to use his formal name in such company. "Pleased to make your aquaintance, Your Majesty. On behalf of The Obelisk, may I assure you of our help and friendship."

"Why, thank you, Rueggan Amadeus Bartholong. You are most welcome here." Vena turned to Boll as if to say, 'What a well-bred fellow he seems,' before turning back to Rueggan. "We hear much good of The Obelisk," she continued. "Are you a spellmaker?"

"I have been known to turn my hand to the Noble Art from time to time," Rueggan replied, humbly.

"Then you may do us a great service," said Vena. Then, turning to the rest of the company, she said, "Please sit, you must be all exhausted. Allow us to offer some refreshment."

They had hardly settled themselves on a conveniently low ledge when several Hydro-Glyphs, bearing diminutive cups, swooped down through the ceiling of mist to set their tiny vessels before the guests.

"Drink," urged Boll, "you will find it most invigorating." Tulan and the other Gadazorri, who had all tasted the Glyph's nectar before, did not hesitate to drain their cups in a single swallow. Rueggan, thinking that these were not exactly what he would call wizard-sized portions, took a small sip, determined to make it last.

"What's wrong, Amadeus Bartholong," enquired Tulan, mischievously, "Is the weight of your name making you slow?" He and the other tried to hide their laughter behind their hands.

"Don't mock, you bunch of dead fish. Just because I happen to have good manners," he returned. Then smiling, Rueggan too drained his cup, amazed by the feeling of warmth which spread rapidly through his limbs and seemed to lift the troubles and tiredness of the last few hectic days from him. He laughed quietly. He had to admit, Rueggan Amadeus Bartholong was a bit of a mouthful.

After a second cup of the nectar, which left them all feeling in better spirits, Boll outlined the nature of Myra's threat to their continued existence. "You see," he said, talking in subdued voice, "the Hydro-Glyphs are unlike any other races. We breathe not only through our noses, but also through our skins. Only here, in the Shadi-Sampi, is the air suitable. That is why, Tulan, I said that I could not return with you to your Raphan. It would have been certain death. We find it difficult enough to tolerate the air in The Delta for more than a day — two at most. So we cannot simply leave here and find somewhere else."

"But I thought you said Myra was doing something or other to your music, not the air" said Rueggan, puzzled.

"I shall explain," replied Boll, "but I thought it best to tell you as much as possible if you are to help me."

"Quite so. Please, excuse my interruption," apologised Rueggan.

"Those who Myra takes from us are changed by the magic given her by this Great One. They may live beyond The Sacred Ring, and can inhabit the area around the Delta without ill-effects. I know not if they can go beyond. This would be a great gift to us but . . . " Boll shook his head, sadly, and held Vena's hand. "The price is too great. Myra can no longer make the music which sustains our souls and protects us from the influence of evil in the air. Without our music, our skin absorbs evil and changes us irreversibly into another form."

"The Thane-Glyphs?" asked Tulan.

"Yes. While we have our music, we cannot be harmed by anything. Not even the power of the Great One could harm us. While we have our music even death shall be unknown." Boll paused and pointed to a small Hydro-Glyph playing beneath one of the waterfalls. "Some day I might be that young again, and she as old as I am now. Then, in time that you would find difficult to imagine, I would grow back into what I am now and she return to an infant playing beneath a waterfall. We move between the extremes of birth and death, but cross into neither."

"But I don't understand," said Rueggan. "I thought Myra was your daughter?"

"They are all my sons and daughters as, one day, I shall be theirs."

"So no Hydro-Glyph is ever born?"

"It is known to us that once, in The Beginning, four were created to dwell in the perfect garden. But two stepped from the path and were cast out. These were the parents of all you who know death. Two did not. It is from these that we came."

"So why the music," Tulan asked, as ever, impatient to get on with things.

"The music purifies us, lifts all evil from within our hearts. But it must be perfect, its harmony without flaw, or the cleansing is incomplete. Myra has placed magical stones outside the ring so that when we play, our music is altered. We cannot cleanse ourselves. Evil is growing amongst us. If it continues, in time we shall all become Thane."

"Why do you not pick up the krystals and take them away?" asked Rueggan.

"Normally we might. But they are filled with evil and to touch them when we have no means of purifying ourselves would change us too quickly."

"Then we shall move them for you," said Tulan, rising to his feet.

"It won't be that easy," said Rueggan. "You can be sure that N'Borg's placed some kind of guard spell upon them. Pick one up and you're likely to end up as part of the mist."

"So what do we do?" Tulan asked.

All eyes turned to the inventor-wizard. "I cannot say until I have seen what effect they produce. The Glyphs must play their music."

"Must we?" said Vena, almost pleading. "It hurts the young ones so."

"I'm afraid you must," confirmed Rueggan. "A more able spellcaster, like Turfen or Shepf, might have been able to sort it out differently, but I need to feel the magic working before I can understand it."

"Then we shall play for you," replied Boll, taking to the air, followed by Vena. "We shall play our music."

"I hope you know what you're doing," said Tulan, apprehensively.

"So do I, my friend. So do I," Rueggan replied, watching as Hydro-Glyphs began to cluster about their King and Queen, high above.

A single note, pure and clear sounded from a tiny flute held by one of the younger Glyphs and, for an instant, Rueggan, for some reason he did not understand, saw an image of himself as a small boy flash before his eyes. As the note swelled in volume, other Glyphs joined in and, soon, the whole of the space between the mist and the place where the wizard stood seemed to take hold of the countless notes, but at the same time, a single note, simultaneously. Then, to the horror of those watching below, a new note appeared from the mist, deep and resonant. It seemed to strike the small Glyph who had begun the music and it fell, spiralling dizzily, its wings no longer able to support its weight, it seemed. In that same instant, Rueggan caught another image which he recognised, once again as himself, only this time he was old, very old indeed. Now the other Glyphs began to fall, like shining leaves stripped from a branch by a cruel wind, landing weakly on the ground about Rueggan and the Gadazorri. The air was torn by a high-pitched scream that Rueggan thought would cause his head to explode, before passing, leaving The Sacred Ring silent save for the moans of the distraught Glyphs. Much to Rueggan's concern, he noticed that many of them had lost almost all their light.

"Well!" demanded Tulan, almost crossly. "Now what? Can you do anthing to help?"

"They must play again," replied Rueggan. "Help them to their feet. They must play again."

"What!" thundered Tulan. "You've all but killed them already!"

"Unless they play again they will all perish," replied Rueggan, with surprising composure. "Get them up!"

As Tulan, against his better judgement, ordered his crew to help the Glyphs to their feet,Rueggan produced a single krystal from beneath his robe and scaled the side of the rock pile, placing the stone carefully upon its apex. "Play! Play!" he shouted down to them.

Several Glyphs slumped back onto the ground as soon as Tulan's crew lifted them. Boll and Vena, their arms clasped together stood supporting each other, weakly.

"It's no use!" Tulan shouted back, his voice tight with emotion. "They're dying!"

One Glyph, who appeared still brighter than the rest, managed to raise himself from the ground. Rueggan watched as he ascended slowly towards the swirling mist above. At first, his flute did not respond. Then, as though summoning his remaining strength, he blew again.

This time a thin, light note sounded out. Silence. An eternity of silence passed before the note returned, still pure and unaltered. The Glyph grew brighter and blew again, this time more forcefully. Again the note went out, and again it returned as a perfect echo. The other Glyphs turned their faces up to stare at the lone musician, their eyes wide in disbelief.

"Play!" boomed Rueggan. "Play for your lives!"

One by one, the Glyphs struggled upwards. One by one, they added their music, growing ever brighter and stronger until, almost beside themselves with relief, Tulan, Rueggan, and the crewmen stood behind a shining host, so bright they charged the mist above with their light. The Perfect Music moved about them, through them and then reached out beyond The Sacred Ring, searching through the darkness of the Shadi-Sampi.

From some way off came a single, piercing scream of rage.

As Rueggan clambered down from the rocks, Tulan raced over to him and slapped him so hard between the shoulders he lost his breath for a moment. "Amazing! Absolutely amazing!" he rejoiced. "What did you do?"

"The krystals were merely inverting the music, Rueggan replied.

"Inverting? . . "

"Turning it all the wrong way round, if you like."

"So? what did you do?"

"Nothing really," said Rueggan, modestly. "Just inverted the inversion so it came out again the right way round."

"Well, whatever you did, it worked. I'll never laugh at your name again!"

"I'll hold you to that," smiled Rueggan. "Or, now I've found my magic touch, perhaps I really will turn you into a dried fish!"

"You wouldn't dare!" laughed Tulan. "At least not until I've got you back to Sobul!"

"There's going to be a scupper full of Snords between us and Sobul, Cap'n," said one of the crewmen. "They'll know we're here after tonight."

"True, but a sharp cutlass is the only magic you need to take care of a Snord," scoffed Tulan. "Besides, how can we fail with Rueggan Amade . . " Rueggan raised a hand above his head and was pretending to incant some spell. "With Rueggan on our side," Tulan corrected, hastily.

The Snord patrol, dawdling in single file high up on the steep green hills which sloped down to the sea to the south of The Delta, were one of many similar parties which had been sent out since the Honji Chief of Operations, General N'Tormet, had learned of the presence of intruders in the swamp. Most of the patrols had centered their search in the area immediately around The Delta, but a few had been given wider-ranging tasks in order to locate any larger enemy encampment which might be waiting to make a move against the General's force.

This particular group of Snords were in high spirits. They were free from the command of their bullying Honji officer and had been given enough supplies to last them several days. These, they had eaten within half a day of leaving, but the hills here were covered with moonberry bushes, and the Snords had scoffed their way to their present position with little intention of returning until they had to.

But not only Snords appreciate the succulent, juicy pulp of moonberries.

Pooks are small, rotund little creatures, with large, black eyes and small, rounded ears. They are incredibly timid and shy and go out of their way not to cross paths with anyone or anything if they can possibly avoid it. Should they be disturbed, Pooks immediately turn onto their backs and, grabbing hold of their long, hairless tails in their tiny forepaws, loop it around the back of their necks and pull. This has the effect of closing them up into a furry ball, with heads, paws and tails tucked safely inside. They remain like this until, certain it is safe to relax their grip upon their tail, they slowly emerge once more.

For one Pook family, happily fattening themselves up in readiness for their long winter sleep, this was destined to be very unpeaceful day. They had the bad fortune to be eating moonberries when the Snord patrol breasted the top of the hill.

Had the Snords been hungry, the Pooks would have unrolled to find themselves inside a Snord stomach. But the Snords were full to bursting (a rare event) and saw the Pooks as offering entertainment rather than sustenance on this occasion.

After amusing themselves by throwing, then kicking the poor Pooks, the Snords hit upon a new game. This involved hurling the smallest Pook a way in front and then attempting to roll the remaining Pooks along the ground towards it. The Snord whose Pook came closest to the small one won the game. The game amused the Snords immensely, especially as their victims uttered high-pitched — though very muffled — 'pooks' of alarm whenever they were rolled.

So absorbed were the Snords in their new game, it might have gone on until darkness fell had not one player, aiming to knock his opponents' Pooks out of the way, fired his Pook-ball with such force it cannoned into three others and then vanished over the edge of the hill with a frightened 'POO-OO-O-O-O-okkk!'

"Aw' That's ruined the game!" complained one of the Snords. "You've lost it now!"

The Snord trotted over to the edge, hoping his Pook had been stopped by a ledge or a bush so that he could retrieve it and continue playing. However, when he poked his snout cautiously over the lip his wicked little eyes lit up in surprise.

"Oi!" he snorted, "Get yer tails over here on the double!"

The rest of the Snords, thinking their comrades had discovered another Pook family, ran over.

"Look what I've found!" grunted the first, excitedly.

Far below, bobbing peacefully at anchor, Tulan's Rahpan impatiently awaited the return of its Captain.

Led by two Hydro-Glyphs and sustained with draughts of their energy-giving nectar, Rueggan and the Gadazorri made quick progress back through the Shadi-Sampi, arriving within striking distance of The Delta within three days. There they bade their guides farewell, Tulan promising that he would return as soon as possible with his fleet to make their traditional rendezvous, and Rueggan that he would send more specialist help when he got back to the Obelisk.

'If I ever get back, that is,' he thought, as soon as the Glyphs had departed. They still had to get to the Skeat without being seen.

"There is an alternative," suggested Tulan, as though reading the wizard's thoughts. "We could always follow the coastline down to the inlet. It would add a day or two onto our journey, but it might be less of a risk."

"I think you're right," agreed Rueggan, "but, much as I like the feel of solid ground beneath my feet, I don't want to delay any longer than is absolutely necessary. The Obelisk needs to know about the situation as soon as possible."

"So, we take the Skeat," affirmed Tulan. "Then I suggest we get ourselves well and truly hidden and wait until dark. We stand no chance of getting through in daylight. We haven't long to wait," he said, locating the sun as a brighted patch glimmering through the close canopy of leaves overhead.

The remainder of the day passed by without event. Twice, a patrol of Snords passed uncomfortably close to the bush in which they were all hidden, but the overpowering smell of stagnation and decay masked the scent of the intruders, and the Snords went on their way without stopping. Soon, the Skinwings began to flit between the trees and the darkness came creeping, advancing slowly like a black tide from the heart of the enchanted swamp.

"Stay close," hissed Tulan. "If we get into trouble, or split up, don't hang around waiting; get back to the Skeat. At least one of us has got to get word to Krellick. Safe voyage."

Taking care over every step, the party darted from shadow to shadow, making their way slowly but surely out onto the split of land where the Skeat lay hidden. Silent as the darkness itself, they slipped past groups of Snords and once, three Honji warriors polishing their long pikes by the light of a fire. Incredibly, they arrived without incident to where the Skeat, still lying as they had left it days before, was pulled up inside the trees.

In the darkness, Tulan montioned that he wanted them to lift the small vessel and carry in down the narrow beach to the waters edge, for fear of its hull scraping across the sand alerting any nearby sentries. At his signal, they lifted as one.

A branch, caught on the Skeat's gunwale, snapped, seeming to split the blanket of silence. They froze, tense, listening, waiting for the sound of feet across the ground they thought must surely come. But once more, the silence descended, and they stepped slowly out onto the beach, stifling their gasps of exertion.

Rueggan could not believe their luck when he felt the cold sea swirl and suck about his legs and, moments later, the Gadazorri plied their oars, each stroke taking them further away from the danger and, Rueggan hoped, closer to home.

"That was easy!" whispered Rueggan, as soon as he thought it safe enough.

"They're even more stupid than I can remember," replied Tulan, reveling in the feel of his small craft's motion upon the water. "We were just too good for them!"

A beam of moonlight glanced momentarily off some polished surface just inside the trees. It moved slightly, then took shape as it stepped out from the shadows. General N'Tormet, flanked by four Honji warriors smiled broadly as he watched the small boat move away from the shore.

"Perhaps we should have taken them, Sir?" ventured one of the Honji.

The General's smile was replaced by a thunderous scowl. "I could pick a grain of sand from beneath my toes that's twice the size of your brain!" he mocked, — the other Honji laughed at their comrade's expense. "They will return to their boat thinking they are safe away," he explained, more to hear himself expound his own wonderful plan than for the instruction of his inferiors. "When something feels safe it relaxes its guard," he continued, his smile returning. "They will not be expecting our visit at all!" He laughed, blackly, before turning and marching back into the trees. "Make sure The Galley is ready and fully armed for the morning," he ordered, "Call me at sunrise."

After a hurried account of events for Krellick's benefit, Tulan and the others fell into their bunks and were soon overcome by the deep, dreamless sleep of exhaustion. Tulan would have slept until the sun was well above the hills had he not been disturbed by something nibbling his toes.

He opened his eyes reluctantly and looked down at the bottom of his bunk. There, crouched over his feet a small furry beast was attempting to bite into his big toe.

"Hey!" he shouted in surprise. "What's going on here?"

Instantly, the creature rolled over onto its back, grabbed its own tail and pulled itself into a tight ball. "Pook!" it said.

"And Pook to you as well! Where have you sprung from?"

"Pook!" it said, again, from somewhere within.

"Go and find your own bed and leave me . . ."

"In the name of The Great One, I demand you surrender your vessel immediately! You are now the prisoners of General N'Tormet, Commander in Chief of N'Borg's Legions! Escape is impossible! Surrender and you will be spared!"

"What!" exclaimed Tulan, springing from his bunk.

"At least for a day or two!" concluded the voice.

Tulan appeared on deck closely followed by Krellick and the rest of the crew, including a very sleepy-eyed Rueggan. To both sides, standing shoulder to shoulder upon the shore, Snords and Honji warriors stood to attention.

"I do hope we have not disturbed your sleep after your busy evening!" said the voice, sarcastically. "Now, do as I say! Surrender!"

Tulan ran up to the bows and looked over. Standing a short distance away upon a large raft of reed bundles floating upon the water, N'Tormet stood, hands on hips. Behind him, four Snords sat clutching long wooden oars uncomfortably.

"Are you the leader?" N'Tormet demanded.

"I am," replied Tulan, still too shocked to think of anything else to say.

"Then turn over your rotten piece of flotsam at once!"

"Drop dead, O great toad of The Ugly One!" returned Tulan. Nobody insulted his ship and got away with it.

"If you do not surrender at once," bellowed N'Tormet, turning purple about the temples, I shall sink you." He smiled, slowly, and pointed out toward's the mouth of the inlet. There, outlined against the brightening sky, was a ship so large for a fleeting moment Tulan mistook it for a huge, square rock.

"With that basket of straw!" scoffed Tulan, still amazed by the sight of so large a vessel. "Don't make me laugh." He looked back at N'Tormet. "You look about as comfortable on the water as a swimmer wearing stone shoes!"

"SURRENDER! NOW!" bellowed N'Tormet.

Tulan did not reply. He ducked down behind the bow, picked up a grappling line and then, with the grace only many seasons of practice can give, swung it overboard. It landed with a thump at N'Tormet's feet.

"Swim for it, fatso!" he jeered, and, giving the line an almighty tug which ripped the hooks free, he sent N'Tormet sprawling backwards. The General's fall was cushioned by two of the Snords who squealed in pain and, in their efforts to escape, kicked the other Snords into the water. The raft rocked crazily, sending shock waves fanning out towards the shore.

"DEATH!" screamed N'Tormet, getting shakily to his feet and pointing his heavy sword at the Rahpan.

"DEATH! DEATH! DEATH!" chanted the Snords and the Honji from the shore, rattling their weapons approvingly.

"Oh, dear!" groaned Rueggan. "Just when I thought I'd get back to my workshop in one piece. I'm getting too old for this sort of thing."

"If he wants a fight, he'll get one, fumed Tulan. Nobody calls my Rahpan names! Nobody!"

"What do you intend doing? asked Rueggan.

Tulan looked first at the shore, then back out to sea where N'Tormet's Battle Galley dominated the skylne between the sloping shoulders of land. "I haven't the faintest idea." he admitted, slumping down miserably onto the polished deck.

"Not one. He's got us caught like a flipskipper in a bottle!"

"Well we'd better come up with something quick, Cap'n," Krellick remarked, impassively, "The Fat one won't take long to paddle back to his ship." he said, watching N'Tormet's raft winding its way unsteadily towards the mouth of the inlet like a drunken fly.

No sooner had N'Tormet reached the safety of his Galley than the sound of a drum echoed along the length of the inlet. Like a gigantic insect, the Galley began to creep slowly forward, the triple ranks of the long oars making it look as though it walked along the water on legs. The Snords on the shore cheered again, and repeated their chorus of "Death! Death!" with even more excitement.

Tulan watched, helplessly. Perhaps he should try and make a run for it. No. He dismissed the idea as soon as it formed. There was hardly room to squeeze a Skeat past the Galley, let alone find room to manouevure the Rahpan, even if he could find space to tack. Then, as he watched, he saw the great ship halt and the oars withdraw.

"Look!" he shouted back to the others, "He hasn't got enough water beneath his keel to come in and get us!"

Tulan's brief moment of relief was soon shattered. There was a sudden clap, followed by a high whistling sound which grew louder.

'SPLUDOOSH!!' A plume of water erupted close to one side of the Rahpan, shooting a fine spray of droplets across the deck.

"What on?" . . . " gasped Tulan, in astonishment.

"Stone me!" exclaimed Rueggan, instantly regretting his choice of words. "They've pinched my idea!"

"What idea?" asked Tulan.

"From the last battle. Don't you remember my catapults?"

Tulan's reply was cut short by another sheet of spray flying over the bows.

"Weigh the anchor!" he shouted, darting for'ard to unfurl the small triangular jib sail. "The least we can do is give them a moving target!"

"Fancy having my idea pinched by the enemy," Rueggan remarked. "They've certainly worked on the design. It's even more powerful than mine were!"

"Got any more bright ideas?" commented Tulan, running past on his way to the helm.

"Actually," replied Rueggan, following after him, "I believe I have."

As Tulan threaded his ship back and forth across the narrow strait of the inlet, turning back from each shore only in time to avoid the hail of stones and the odd pike rained upon them by N'Tormet's forces. Rueggan attempted to explain his idea.

"Sewing? Sewing!" exclaimed Tulan when the wizard was finished. "We're fighting for our lives and you ask me if I can sew! You've finally flipped!"

"I believe it can work," replied Rueggan, undaunted. "Have you a better idea, or are you going to scuttle back and forth all day? They're bound to score a hit eventually, you know."

"Sewing!" Tulan reiterated. "That's work for females!"

"Not when you don't have one," said Krellick. "What do you want me to sew, wizard? I'm pretty good with a sail needle."

"Thank you," replied Rueggan, flinching as another boulder whistled just above the deck, "Cut the mainsail loose and get any other spare sail you've got up on deck."

"Hey! Keep your hands off my sails!" shouted Tulan, overhearing Rueggan's request.

"Why? You won't be needing them much longer if you don't let me try," Rueggan returned.

"He's right, Cap'n," said Krellick, after passing amongst the crew and ordering them to do whatever the wizard told them.

Tulan forgot all about the wizard as he and two deckhands were left alone to concentrate on dodging the flying boulders launched from the Galley. Rueggan's prediction almost came true when one of the missile's caught the main mast, snapping it like a dead twig, sending a shudder the length of the ship and showing the sewers with splinters.

"I don't suppose I'll be needing my mainsail after all," Tulan shouted. Nobody replied. They were all far too busy stitching.

"That's it!" cried Rueggan, springing to his feet. "Now all I need is a couple of big stones."

"Hold on and I'll try and catch one for you," Tulan laughed, darkly. "First sewing, now stone! This is a ship, not dry land!"

"The ballast, Cap'n," Krellick suggested.

"We'll wobble all over the place if you take it out," Tulan returned.

"I only want two. I estimate that's as much as I'll be able to carry," said Rueggan.

Tulan looked at Krellick and shrugged. "Why not? He's had nearly everything else."

"Right, stop the ship!" said Rueggan.

"Why, do you want to get off?" asked Tulan.

"I do," Rueggan replied, "I do indeed."

"This I've got to see," whispered Tulan, behind his beard.

"What are you doing with my robe basket?" asked Tulan, recognizing his possession peeking from beneath a pile of stitched sail.

"You shall see," said Rueggan, sounding much more confident than he really was.

The Rahpan was hit a glancing blow which knocked them all off their feet.

"Get on with it!" ordered Tulan.

"Stand clear," Rueggan replied, placing the two large stones in Tulan's basket before climbing in himself. Now . . . " he took out another krystal from beneath his robe. "My last one," he observed. "I hope it works . . . "

"He hopes it works! He hopes!" Tulan groaned.

"Well, I've never tried it on this scale before," replied Rueggan. "And in the circumstances, what with boulders whizzing past my ears . . . "

"Alright! Alright!" dismissed Tulan. "We've no time for explanations now."

Holding the krystal upon the palm of his hand, Rueggan muttered some spellwords. The krystal flashed brightly, dazzling the crew with its light. "Now," said Rueggan, holding his hand beneath the sail, "if the krystal can superheat the air trapped inside this sail bag it should begin to .... Yes, see, it's working already .... It should begin to inflate."

The crew, Tulan in particular, gasped as the part of the mainsail bearing the purple fish emblem began to swell and lift itself clear of the deck as though alive. "I will take off and float over the enemy Galley, whereupon I shall drop the stones down into the middle of their ship. Hopefully, this will create two holes large enought to sink it," Rueggan continued, as though lecturing a group of Apprentices.

"I am dreaming. Tell me I am dreaming," said Tulan, watching as more of the sail bag rose up into the air.

Rueggan smiled. "Remember me telling you in Sobul that I thought there was another way of travelling to the Shadi-Sampi? ... "

"I do," laughed Tulan.

"And talking about how far away the stars really were ... "

"Yes."

"Well, I did hope that this little idea would help me to find out ... "

Before Tulan could say anything else, the sail bag, Tulan's robe basket, and Rueggan, lifted clear of the deck and began to rise.

On the shore, an audible gasp of amazement came from the enemy ranks. On the Galley too, the ascent of Rueggan was watched with open-mouthed surprise and wonder. The bombardment ceased abruptly. What was this? A huge purple fish that could fly? What was it going to do?

Rueggan's greatest moments of triumph also have the uncanny knack of being his most short-lived. This, perhaps his most remarkable achievement, was to prove no exception. There were two things he had not taken into account.

The first was the means of controlling his direction once he was airborne. There was not a breath of wind. Rueggan simply continued to rise vertically above the Rahpan.

The second was, to be fair, outside his control. Not only those engaged in the confrontation in and around the narrow inlet saw the round purple fish. As he cleared the backs of the hills Rueggan caused another look of surprise. N'Grall, N'Borg's Henchdragon and terror of the skies, on his way to the Delta, saw him too. Exactly what this strange beast was, the dragon had no idea. But if it flew, it could also be shot down. Nothing, absolutely nothing, would be allowed to challenge his domination of the air! With a tilt of his huge wings, N'Grall wheeled in for the kill.

Rueggan saw him first, and turned several shades lighter behind his beard. Next, the crowd on the shore saw him and cheered vociferously. There was going to be a fight! N'Tormet did not smile —the dragon had a nasty habit of stealing his hard-earned glory within the space of a single bolt of flame. Already the Snords in the Galley were starting to cheer the one come to save them from the purple fish. Neither did those on board the Rahpan smile. N'Grall could turn their vessel to a cinder in moments.

As he closed in, N'Grall saw the wizard standing in the basket beneath the sail bag. He circled cautiously. He recognised Rueggan of old. He was the one who had knocked N'Grall unconscious at The Obelisk with a stone from one of those wretched catapults. Yes. That had been a constant irritation ever since. N'Grall had lost face in front of those pathetic Snords. They had trampled over him as he lay on the ground. Of all the wizards he hated — and he hated them all — this was the one he hated the most!

"So wizard, we meet again at last!" he thundered, flashing over Rueggan's sail bag in a blur of wings, almost too quickly for the eye to follow. He banked sharply and turned. There seemed no threat to him here. On the contrary, the round thing appeared to have no life of its own. "You think to take to the air now?" N'Grall cut past, closer this time, still cautious.

"How's your headache?" provoked Rueggan. He might as well get an insult or two in before he was fried, he thought.

"What!" boomed N'Grall, two plumes of flame curling about his snout.

"The last time I saw you, you were being trodden on by Snords," shouted Rueggan. Words were the only ammunition he had left.

"The last words of a meddling spell maker," hissed the dragon, between his teeth.

"Do give my ears a rest, you over-grown worm," replied Rueggan. "I've heard it all before."

Rueggan saw N'Grall's throat thicken as the dragon summoned up a flame bolt from within his furnace. The inventor-wizard closed his eyes and thought about his workshop far away in Wendlock . . .

Rueggan felt his whiskers shrivel as a blast of heat swept over him. A scream of pain and outrage. Then another voice. One he recognised.

"That's for Nimbo!"

Rueggan opened his eyes in time to see Groosh rocket skywards. N'Grall, one flank blackened and scorched, shot beneath the basket, almost tipping Rueggan out. Then another blur of wings as Jeptha swooped past close on the Henchdragon's tail. Rueggan turned. There, dropping from the sky, wings folded, young Skit fell, unleashing a compact fireball that caught N'Grall on a wingtip. Below, the Gadazorri were cheering and clapping wildly. "By my beard!" was the only thing Rueggan could think of to say.

N'Grall could better any other dragon for power and speed in the air. Of all the dragons in Cairn Tor, only Groosh could match him for skill and agility, but lacked the Henchdragon's awesome firepower. Had he seen them coming, it would have been a close contest but, surprised and already wounded, N'Grall was, for once, on the defensive. After hurling a couple of warning bolts at his assailants, he bolted for the sanctuary of The Waste of Shugg, where no other dragon save he could fly, Groosh, Jeptha and Skit giving chase.

From the Galley, another boulder came hurtling through the

air to land in a cloud of spray behind the Rahpan. N'Tormet was eager to return to business now that the dragons were out of the way!

"Are you going to do something other than enjoy the view?" Tulan shouted up to Rueggan.

"Awfully sorry," Rueggan apologised. "It seems I'm stuck!"

Another boulder splashed close by.

"Well I'm not being a sitting target any longer," shouted Tulan. "Let's get moving again!"

Rueggan sighed. After everything, they were still up to their ears in trouble. And now here he was, stuck in mid-air powerless to do anything but admire the view . . . What was that? There, out to sea. He screwed up his eyes. Then he blinked hard. Yes! It was! It really was!

"Tulan! Tulan!" he shouted. "They're coming! The Gadazorri are coming!" Rueggan sat in the bottom of the basket and closed his eyes. He was determined not to look again. The way things had gone today, the whole fleet was likely to sink before it got here!

N'Tormet saw them too, and cursed loudly. Life was downright unfair! Here he was, in the middle of nowhere, with a small army and a Battle Galley at his disposal against a single, half-crippled, half-crewed boat, and a whole fleet shows up!

"Sound the withdrawal!" he ordered. "Quickly!"

A deep, protracted note sounded from the Galley and, instantly, the Snords and Honji on both shores of the inlet began to run toward the place where the two opposing hills came closest to each other. N'Tormet hardly waited for his forces to board from one side and then the other, before turning to Galley and heading off towards The Delta at top speed.

"We're saved!" shouted Rueggan, gleefully. "I can go home at last!"

"One small problem . . . " Tulan shouted up.

"Dear me, yes," replied Rueggan. "I'd not given a thought to getting back down again!"

N'Grall is thwarted at the last moment!

"We'll have to leave you a while," apologised Tulan. "I'll have to go out or they'll chase the Galley and we mightn't see them again for days."

"But they're bound to see me," objected Rueggan.

"Exactly. I think if I saw a great bag floating in mid-air with a wizard sitting in a rope basket underneath it, I'd sail on," laughed Tulan.

"But the purple fish . . ." pleaded Rueggan, pointing a the emblem. "They're sure to recognise that!"

"Sit quietly. You've caused me enough trouble since I met you in Sobul!" Tulan, Krellick and the rest of the crew laughed, and set the jib sail to take them slowly out to meet their kinsfolk.

"Well that's gratitude for you!" said Rueggan to himself. He sat down in the basket, rested his chin on his knees, and was asleep before Tulan had reached the open sea.

The wind, which had been blowing steadily from the southeast, over the top of the hills, suddenly veered and freshened, coming off the sea and down the inlet. It pushed against the sail bag gently, as though enquiring. But the wind has seen and will go on seeing stranger things than Rueggan's invention, and pushed it slowly inland without a second thought.

Tulan watched helplessly as his friend disappeared from sight. There was nothing he could do apart from wave. But there would be other times. Now, he must see to his own affairs. The Snords and Honji who had been deserted by their General as he fled back through the Blind Sea would have to be driven out from The Delta —that was if they hadn't already left of their own accord. The orchid-spices would have to be collected from the Hydro-Glyphs and, after that, they would have to find safe anchorage before winter closed in. Perhaps then, Tulan would have enough time to build a new Rahpan — he was certainly in need of one!

Now there was an idea! He would build a Rahpan as large as N'Tormet's Galley. Now the Great One had discovered how to use the sea, he was sure to continue to build new Galleys and, some day, they would almost certainly come into conflict again. It was wise to think of the future. Perhaps Rueggan would show him how to install a catapult? Yes, the wizard owed him at least that in return for his sail. He would send a letter with the next dragon they met and address it to Rueggan Amadeus Bartholong!

"Rueggan! Rueggan!"

The wizard awoke with a start to find himself staring at Groosh's underside as the dragon glided effortlessly above him.

"Where did everybody go? How did I get here?" asked Rueggan, sticking his nose over the edge of the basket. "More's to the point, where exactly is here?"

"What's this thing?" enquired Groosh.

"A new invention," Rueggan answered proudly. "And it works!"

"I can see that, but if I were you I wouldn't let Grunch find out. He's likely to think you're after his customers."

"Not much chance of that," replied Rueggan. "I can't even steer it. It's got a will of its own. Anyway, you didn't answer my question, where am I?"

"At this speed, I'd say about two days from The Obelisk. If the wind doesn't change, that is."

"Where's Jeptha and young Skit?"

"They've gone ahead to give their report. There'll be quite a reception waiting for you, I should imagine."

"I suppose there will," said Rueggan, thoughtfully, then added, "Do you think you could give me a tow?"

"My pleasure," Groosh replied. "Catch hold of my tail. Next stop, The Obelisk."

"I'd rather not, if you don't mind, I want to see my workshop. It seems so long since I was last there. Besides, I want to check up on the Gorphs."

"They've been giving that Apprentice, Gwillum, a right runaround." Groosh smiled.

"I don't want to know," replied Rueggan. "I really don't want to."

Rueggan returned to the ground, thanks to a well-placed puncture from one of Groosh's talons, just beyond his workshop. From within, came the sound of crashing and banging, and Gwillum's voice, pleading, "No! No! Not that!" followed by another loud crash.

"It's so good to be back," Rueggan sighed.

THE MAGIC BOTTLE

The storm had passed. Already the sky was clearing — widening patches of aquamarine beginning to appear amidst the rapidly thinning banks of grey cloud. At the top of the beach, where the rain had pock-marked the dry sand, a young boy sat beneath a rock overhang, watching passively as drips from the rock mass over him fell down and exploded in a shower of smaller droplets upon the bald head of a weed-wrapped boulder. At his feet, fast asleep, lay a small creature whose fur-covered skin appeared to be several sizes to big — as though its current owner had loaned it from a rightful encumbent of much greater dimensions.

"Come on, you flea-ridden sack of bones, the rain has stopped!" the boy said, dealing a sharp kick to the snoring creature's rump.

The creature stirred and yawned cavernously, displaying purple gums lined with large, yellowing teeth, before staring myopically, first at the boy — now up on his feet — and then at the expanse of pebble-strewn sand. Slowly, as though it required considerable concentration and effort, the creature raised itself up onto its haunches and inclined its head in order to better scratch behind an ear with its hind paw.

"Wake up, Ottho!" the boy urged, impatiently. "It'll soon be time to go back home!"

At the mention of the word 'home', Ottho dragged himself unwillingly to his feet, slowly wagging his excuse of a tail and regarding the boy with a look which amounted to, 'That's the best idea you've had all day!'

"Seek!" commanded the boy, pointing along the beach. "Seek, you insult to the good name of your parents!"

Ottho appeared completely immune to the boy's remonstrations and simply scratched his other ear with exaggerated slowness, his eyes half-closed with appreciation.

"Stay here then," said the boy, finally running out of patience with his uncooperative accomplice. "Stay here until your bones are as white and dry as driftwood. I'll get myself another Snoofer, you see if I don't!" He turned and marched resolutely down the beach towards the sea.

Ottho sighed deeply and set out after the boy, breaking into a trot that seemed to cause the loose folds of fur to slide down the length of his back and gather like discarded sacking about his hindquarters. Within moments he overtook the boy and began to quarter the beach; nose pressed to the sand, tail stub held stiffly erect. If he found something worthwhile, perhaps Klip would be satisfied and they could go back to Sobul? A bowlful of scraps, a comfortable old blanket and a long, uninterrupted sleep were Ottho's idea of pure bliss. Now, where was that nice Blueback he had sniffed out yesterday? . . . He had neglected to draw it to Klip's notice then. It was always best to keep one or two in reserve as a hedge against a bad day or, as now, when he felt like an early supper.

Klip was one of a small band of boys in Sobul who, lacking the necessary family connections, had failed to get himself apprenticed to one of the tradesmen when he had Come of Age. He had not much liked the idea of wasting his youth trying to work his way up through the ranks of Civil Servants in the cloisters of the Assembly Hall, or as a price-runner in the fish market and, using all of his meagre savings, had purchased Ottho from a retired Snoofer breeder after being assured of the excellent pedigree which was certain to mark out Ottho as a Snoofer of superior manners and bearing.

In a very short space of time, Ottho left Klip in no doubt that he was not going to fulfill any of the promise attending his aristocratic birth — in fact, he appeared determined to revolt against the sensibilities of his forbears and, whenever the opportunity presented itself, went out of his way to show himself a Snoofer of unparalleled uncouthness. He gulped his food — which considerably enhanced his potential for belching at inopportune moments — slobbered copiously, impressed his filthy paws upon the clothes of the well-dressed, made overtly amorous advances to any female Snoofers that were unfortunate enough to cross his path and, Klip suspected, had even agreed to sub-let space in his fur — so well tennanted was it by a host of hopping, creeping and crawling occupants!

But Ottho had one outstanding asset. (When he could be cajoled or bullied into using it). Never was there a Snoofer born with a keener sense of smell.

Now there are a few craftsmen in Sobul who make a good living by cutting, polishing and reshaping shells and turning them into extremely attractive brooches and clasps. In the main, these are often used to brighten up a plain robe, or add the finishing touch to a young girl's best (or only) dress. But the most beautiful shells — those which seem to capture the light-changing emerald hues of the sea and the faultless blue of the sky — are also the rarest, and command a high trade value when made into emblems marking out the wearer as one in high office, or betokening social status. When Klip accidentally discovered Ottho's talent for sniffing out and uncovering these rarities buried on an isolated stretch of beach some distance outside the settlement, he was quick to turn it to his advantage.

At first, the craftsmen had, due to their experience as traders and the boy's need to provide both himself and his Snoofer with at least one good meal a day, got the better of the exchange. However, though his clothes were dull, Klip's mind certainly was not, and he soon learned to play one craftsman off against the other until he was sure the exchange rate was a fair one. Had Klip chosen, he could have lived to a better standard than any of his apprenticed peers but, here again, the boy showed remarkable foresight for one so young. He realised that what kept the price of his shells so high was their scarcity. Were he to trade every shell of worth he found, their value would soon fall. To this end he kept back the most perfect specimens, hiding them deep within a crevice inside a narrow mouthed sea-cave which could only be reached when the tide was at its lowest ebb. Only occasionally, when one of the craftsmen received a special — and well rewarded — commission would he trade in one of his secret cache and reap the benefits associated with high demand

and limited supply. His secret collection would, one day, allow him to retire from shell-collecting and spend the rest of his days as he wished.

Of course, Klip's success came to the notice of other occupants in Sobul. The craftsmen tried to have him followed in order to discover both the location and the method by which he came by the shells but, having expected this, Klip noticed he was being shadowed and promptly returned to Sobul and let it be known that he would stop all supplies until the spies were removed. He had, he threatened, a wealthy friend who was considering starting his own shell-shaping business who would be only too happy to take advantage of his service ... Then, some of the apprenticed boys — noticably those who had gloated when Klip failed to find an apprentice position — waylaid him and threatened to give him a good beating if he did not give them a cut from his trading profits. Fortunately, Ottho had chosen that moment to show that he was not entirely without scruples and had punctured the seats of their breeches with his teeth and driven them away in a frenzy of snapping, snarling and growling. (Such an uncharacteristic amount of effort had, however, resulted in him being even more reluctant than usual to move from his blanket for the next few days).

A few did try to compete on more respectable terms, and traded for a Snoofer of their own. For several days a small pack of Snoofers set out from Sobul with their owners early in the morning, full of hope and expectation, and returned tired, disappointed and shell-less. Once, Klip had followed them, sitting on a rock at the top of the beach as the Snoofer pack and their handlers scoured the sand like large, animated insects. Ottho had watched with an air of detachment, snorting disdainfully whenever a male Snoofer passed close enough to be insulted, and adopting a very superior air when a female Snoofer was close enough to be impressed. With a sense of theatrical timing, Ottho had waited until the would-be shell collectors were at their most despondent, and then rose to his feet, strolled unhurriedly into their midst, and dug up a

Blueback, returning and dropping it at Klip's feet: something he had steadfastly refused to do before or since.

It was the final straw. Snoofers and handlers had turned and gone back to Sobul to try and find some other occupation in which they were not so hopelessly outclassed, leaving Klip and Ottho to go about their business without interruption.

Klip's secret cache had grown steadily, and he confidently expected to be able to retire from shell collecting by the end of his twentieth full season cycle — five season cycles distant — Then Ottho could sleep and eat his fill. For all his unkind words, Klip was not the sort to trade off his Snoofer as though he were merely another asset. Ottho had earned a share in any reward which came Klip's way. But, until then, he and Ottho would have to apply themselves to their work. This explained why, today, when the rain had whipped across the beach, Klip had decided to wait it out, and had not returned to Sobul for an early supper.

"Seek, Ottho! Seek!" he urged.

"I'm seeking! I'm seeking!' Ottho thought, without lifting his nose from the sand. 'Where is that Blueback? I could have sworn it was two strides to the left of that big rock . . . Perhaps the tide's moved it up the beach a couple of paces? . . . What a confounded nuisance! . . . '

Klip, who all the time had been watching Ottho closely, suddenly caught a flash of reflected light in the corner of his eye. Instinctively he turned, looking towards the sea.

There it was again. His eye was drawn to something small and dark framed in the flat expanse of white froth where the waves fanned out across the sand.

What was it? Wet driftwood? No, somehow its movement was different. It bobbed more readily to the surface whenever a wave bore down upon it, and reflected sunlight too sharply.

Klip stepped out into the sea, wading through the shallow, sand-warmed water, and plucked the object from the surf. Behind him, Ottho yapped — he had found the Blueback — but Klip's attention was focussed completely upon the small object he held. It was some kind of vessel and, through its translucent walls, he could see something else, trapped within. A piece of parchment. Yes, he was almost positive it was parchment. He could make out what he took to be a wax seal on one side; similar to the one used by the Fugleman of Sobul on official correspondence.

He strode back to the beach, holding up his find so that the sun illuminated its semi-opaque interior. Why had someone bothered to put a parchment inside a container? Perhaps it had fallen overboard from a Gadazorri Rahpan? There was one way to find out.

Kneeling down and placing the container on the sand before him. Klip began to pull at the stopper sealing off its narrow neck, with his fingernails. It was tight, and he redoubled his efforts, at length feeling the stopper begin to shift. In the same instant, a blinding flash lifted him up into the air and threw him backwards, dumping him ungracefully on the sand.

Ottho, the Blueback clamped in his jaws, came bounding over to his prostrate master, the coarse hairs along the ridge of his back held stiffly erect.

"It's alright," Klip assured, rasing himself up onto one elbow and looking at the container in astonishment. "There's no harm done."

Ottho walked over and sniffed the vessel, growling ferociously. "Leave it," ordered Klip, scrambling to his feet. "Leave Ottho!"

The Snoofer complied, and retreated a few paces before lying down with his snout between his forepaws, still growling.

Klip picked up the container gingerly and shook it. The parchment rattled dryly inside. "It's protected by magic," he concluded. "I don't think it will allow itself to be opened by just anyone."

Klip weighed the container in his hand. Should he toss it back into the sea and forget all about it? Or, perhaps, he should hide it with his shell cache? Yes, that was a better idea. He had heard that a spellcaster from The Council had stayed in Sobul recently and would be returning with the Gadazorri quite soon.

He might be interested in it. It was obvious that someone had gone to a lot of trouble to make sure the container's secret would be kept safe from any but a spellcaster. If he was lucky, the wizard from The Council might be willing to reward Klip handsomely. Yes, he would hide it with the shells in the sea-cave and await for the wizard's return . . .

*…ip's discovery of a simple bottle may prove to be more valuable than the rarest shell . . . but
…y a wizard can unlock its secret.*